Date Due

the
man
who
wanted
to
save
Canada

OTTAWA (CP) — Neil Brody is a man who wants to save Canada.

At a time when the nation's constitutional future appears in doubt, many Canadians may share the sentiment.

But few would do what Brody did: take out a full page ad to express his feelings to Canada at large.

The ad, which appeared in five leading Canadian dailies earlier this week, called on Canadians to "assume power for their own direction and destiny."

Who is this would-be prophet?

Published by

HOOT PRODUCTIONS

Victoria, B.C. / 1975

the
man
who
wanted
to
save
Canada

A Prophetic Novel by

R. J. CHICK CHILDERHOSE

ISBN NUMBER 0-919994-00-8

Published by
HOOT PRODUCTIONS
303 - 625 Admirals Road
Victoria, British Columbia

DESIGN: Bev Leech

Printed and bound in Canada by
MORRISS PRINTING COMPANY LTD.
Victoria, British Columbia

because
of
Marj

Books by R. J. Chick Childerhose

ADULT NOVELS
Splash One Tiger
Winter Racehorse
The Man Who Wanted to Save Canada

JUVENILE NOVELS
Fighter Pilot
Hockey Fever in Goganne Falls

SHORT STORIES
F-86 Sabre

Chapter 1

The life-force that had vitalized Neil Brody, set him apart and made him unique, was ebbing. It was dark, he was sick. Chills alternated with sweat-drenching fevers. Under him was a scratchy woollen blanket.

In hazy moments of awareness he tried to visualize his surroundings. The bed was a bunk. The room, he sensed, was a cell. A phone rang unanswered somewhere in the building. It brought back the memory of the call that had ultimately brought him here.

When the phone rang that day Lin Lee had answered it. "Mister Brody?" he said, "right here." As he handed the receiver across the desk he told Brody: "Sounds like Henri's secretary . . . if it's him, say hello for me."

Henri Robillard, and Lin Lee, had served in Brody's squadron during World War II. Following the war Henri and Brody had both joined the federal civil service. When Brody left Ottawa to join Lee in business in the Northwest Territories, Henri had kept in touch with them.

"Business is terrible," Brody now told their friend. "Do you want to buy us out?"

Though Brody's tone was bantering, his bitterness was real. When the development of oil fields and navigable sea routes made it profitable to do so, the base metal mines of the Territories were promptly relocated on the northern fringes of the continent.

The loss of the area's only industrial payroll had collapsed every mining community but Yellowknife . . . which had the government payroll. Brody's appeals to the corporate consciences of the mining companies had been futile.

"Can I come to Ottawa?" Brody glanced at his partner as he said it. "Sure. Is there money involved?"

The call was a coincidence. Brody had planned to visit Henri in Ottawa prior to departing from Canada anyway. But he didn't tell Henri that. "What is the job?"

A look of surprise came over his face. "Sounds like a practical joke." And a moment or two later: "Today . . . you'll see me tomorrow. Okay? Oh, Lin says hello . . . yes, the same: inscrutable." He laughed, said goodbye and listened for the connection to break.

"How's that for timing?" he said, handing the receiver back to Lee.

Lee was tall for a Chinese, as tall as Brody. He wore hornrim glasses which accentuated his quiet intelligence. "What did he want?"

"There's a dead bird on his desk. Someone sent it to him."

"To External Affairs? Why?"

"Henri doesn't know."

"Does he think *you* do?"

Brody was in his late-fifties; he appeared early-forties. The attributes of a wartime leader were still his: strength, confidence and honesty backed by intellect. The unmilitary part was the long auburn hair that covered his neck.

"Henri thinks I might find out," he said.

"Maybe you'll come back," Lee changed the subject. "John Ahvakana says the Brotherhood would like you to run for Council again."

The offer referred to Brody's years on the Territorial Council. Brody had fought so hard for Native Rights, and so tenaciously against the developers and despoilers of the North, that eventually he'd been ousted from the Council by the White Power Movement. The success of this group had disenfranchised the 80 per cent of the Northwest Territories' population who were non-white and, mostly, non-educated.

The offer of support by the Brotherhood of Natives was appreciated by Brody, one of the few whites in the Territories to speak most of the many dialects.

"The Brotherhood should elect native leaders," Brody said slowly, "damn tough leaders."

"You think they'll ever control the Council?"

The Territorial Council was funded by Ottawa and run by a senior civil servant. It was ignored by Ottawa on all major decisions affecting the Territories.

"The Northwest 'Terrified' Council?" Brody shrugged. "There won't be a Province of the Mackenzie until the exploitation is complete."

Ottawa showed no intention of sharing the $1 billion per year it made in royalties from the oil and gas finds in the Arctic with the people of the North.

"We'll miss you," Lee said. "New Zealand is a long way."

"I know." Brody's strong hand brushed his hair back in a habitual gesture. It assured him the back of his neck was still covered.

Lee stood up. "If you're catching that nine a.m. flight we'd better go."

They left the small tin building that was warehouse, workshop and office for Brody and Lee Aviation. The company pickup truck was parked alongside but instead of heading for it, Brody strode along their dock. He paused under a vast, projecting slab of maroon metal wing. The wing was attached to a World War II flying boat called *The Queen.*

The Queen was recognizably a Canso. But anyone familiar with Cansos would have been horrified at what had happened to her. Brody's modifications had been endless and cumulative. He was an innovator, and an innovator is a man who cannot rest with a simply good idea . . . it must always and forever be improved upon.

Now he was regarding the maze of angle irons and pulleys that surmounted the rear hatch. He'd designed it — and it worked perfectly — for raising stretcher cases horizontally from the ground to where the crew could move them inside the plane.

Lee was standing at his elbow. "You want to make *more* changes to it?" he chided, indicating the welded and rewelded ironwork.

"No," chuckled Brody. "I was just thinking . . . " He didn't finish. Instead, he started for the truck.

From a distance people couldn't tell the partners apart. Both were flat-bellied and muscular, the result of years of ceaseless physical labour. Both climbed the high perches of *The Queen* with an ease that made difficult chores seem like leisure activity.

9

Lee stopped the truck at the top of the rise to let Brody view a familiar scene for the last time. On the muddy Hay River barges, tugs and float planes bobbed along the various wooden docks. To the north and east was Great Slave. The early sun lay a swath of molten gold across the restless grey-green swells. The swells would get higher as the wind picked up, as it would.

Driving along Hay River's main street Lee remarked: "Lot of changes since we came up here."

Irritation clouded his hazel-green eyes and Brody rubbed the back of his neck. "Changes, all right," he rumbled. "They've polluted the Mackenzie, the Yukon, Great Slave, 'Bear . . . destroyed every wildlife sanctuary from Hay to Tuk'." He looked at his partner, bristling. "For what?"

"For money, Neil," Lee said quietly.

The passenger cabins of the jetliners he rode in were grubby. Cigarette butts, cellophane wrappings, gum and candy bar debris littered the floors. Cabin service was a plastic cup of coffee.

On the flight to Winnipeg the woman in the next seat had a comment to make about the headline story in the newspaper he was reading. It concerned Quebec's latest bargaining demands for a divorce.

"You watch," she said, reaching across and tapping his paper for emphasis, "Ottawa will give them everything they want. And when they've got that, the Frogs will decide on a whole new list of things . . . and they'll get those, too!"

"Do you think so?" Brody murmured politely.

"Think so?" snorted the woman, picking up her own paper to conclude the conversation. "I *know* so."

Looking out the window during the stop at Winnipeg, Brody noted the decay outside the terminal building. The pitted and broken concrete. The ramp vehicles with engine covers missing. Paper trash lining the steel mesh fences and filling the scoop jet-wash barriers.

He wondered whether the decline was due to mismanagement, the depression, or perhaps a subconscious protest by the workers. He had a mental image of a mechanic sabotaging the plane he was in. Sabotage had replaced strikes.

On the last leg of his journey — Winnipeg to Ottawa — he was reading a Toronto paper. The page he was viewing featured a photo-article on Canada's Armed Forces. The text told the reader how handy it was that French-speaking troops were already organized into units, and these units would become the Quebec Armed Forces.

"Those bastards!" said the man next to him.

Brody turned to look at him. The man was his own age, but fat. He looked like a businessman. The man pointed angrily at the story Brody had been reading. "If our army had any balls we'd go in there and clean them out!"

"Who?"

"The Separatistes. They're the ones causing the trouble."

"Oh." Brody hesitated, wanting to mention that most of the Quebec people had voted for the Quebec Liberation Party. He remained silent.

"Do you know?" said the man, leaning toward Brody in a confidential manner. "I am ashamed of my country."

"Because it may break up?"

"No. Because English-Canadians won't fight for it."

The man sat back, stretched his feet and regarded him. "We should invade them, subdue them, and keep this country together," he said firmly.

Brody wondered how many Canadians felt the same way. He suggested, mildly, that the world had enough violence without Canada adding a civil war.

"Ah," said the man waving him off with a pudgy hand and closing his eyes as an end argument, "that's the *real* problem: people like you willing to let our country go down the drain."

Waiting for him to get off the plane was Henri Robillard. His long-time friend had changed but little. The coal black curls had grey in them, but the dark eyes and alert expression remained the same. He was of medium height and build, which made him look small beside Brody.

Henri — his one-time flight engineer, now diplomat — was delighted to see him.

"I was coming to see you anyway," Brody said. And then added: "Dressed that way you make me feel like a foreign dignitary."

Henri was wearing the standard Department of External Affairs dark suit and pastel shirt. His smile was one of gratitude and pleasure. "You noticed," he said, glancing down at the old-fashioned tie he was wearing. Since most of it was hidden by his vest he used two fingers to plump the exposed portion of the tie out.

The drab tie, which was a crinkly royal blue with gold specklings woven through, contrasted with Henri's fastidious taste in clothing.

"You recognize it," Henri said, happiness in his dark eyes.

Brody rifled his memory banks, wondering if he'd given the tie to Henri. He hadn't, of course. Henri, whose sensitivity bordered on prescience, realized that Brody had forgotten.

"The squadron tie," he said sadly. He started toward the luggage recovery area. "You forgot."

"I never bought one," admitted Brody who abhorred all such affectations.

As they left his hotel Brody noticed the nearby houses. They were brick; they contrasted with the flimsy frame bungalows and 'mobile' homes he was used to in the northern settlements.

Stacked-up piles of uncollected garbage bags lined the curbs. Pets with sharp claws had ripped the bags and strewn the contents.

"Why don't they pick up the garbage?" Brody asked. "Is there a strike?"

Henri glanced up at him. There was a trace of irony in his voice. "Strikes in the social sector are illegal now, didn't you know?"

"No," admitted Brody, wondering how he could have missed such a legislative event.

"Part of the Civil Unrest Act."

"Civil *Unrest* Act?" Brody had not heard of it. The stink of the garbage reminded him of his question. "What's that got to do with garbage collection?"

"You're wondering why, in this day of mass unemployment, workers won't work?"

"It's a job, isn't it?"

"Government froze the wage scales but failed to freeze prices.

City workers were already low paid; they couldn't keep up with inflation."

The phone booth was hot; but the noise and the fumes of Ottawa's traffic required a closed door.

"Is the Minister in?" Brody asked.

"May I say to her who's calling please?" The secretary had a French accent.

"Neil Brody."

He wondered, as he waited, whether Jan Stewart had forgotten him.

"Neil?" There was spontaneous pleasure in her voice. "Have you finally come out of the North Woods?"

He tried to visualize the young Vietnam War protester as what she was now: Minister of Research and Development. "Yes," he said. "I was afraid you might not remember me."

"Never forget a friend, Neil." Her voice was warm. "Am I going to see you?"

"Are you married?" Brody asked.

"No . . . are you?"

"Once was enough," he said fervently.

"I guess your kids are all grown up now."

"Yes . . . and scattered. Did you know I'm a grandfather?"

"No!" She laughed, then: "What brings you to Ottawa?"

"Henri Robillard; I'm doing some work for him."

"Robillard . . . with External?"

"Yes. When do I get to see you? This evening?"

"I'm sorry, Neil." There was regret in her sigh. "It's this Quebec secession thing . . . the House is sitting in emergency debate."

She gave him her home phone number and they agreed to get together later in the week.

"It's emotional," Brody told Henri in the restaurant that evening. "English-speaking Canadians just never believed it would happen."

The table they were seated at was so small the candle vase and condiments occupied half of it. The waitress returned to fill their cups. Henri thanked her, then renewed their conversation.

"I think the Quebecois were surprised too. But now that it's done, now that their government has applied for secession . . . they are happy."

"Hard times coming in Quebec."

"No," Henri corrected. "Quebec has only known hard times, from the very first. It's the hard times in the rest of Canada that bothers the English."

"Well, English Canada is going to make things even tougher for you people in Quebec."

"I know; they hate us."

"They feel . . . " Brody groped for the right feeling, "let down."

"They feel a lot of things," Henri said morosely. "But Neil, the desire for independence exists in every French-Canadian heart. It always has."

"Will you be going with Quebec?"

"Yes. The family is already established. I commute to Quebec City on the weekends."

Brody stared at the glowing glass vase which was a candle crematorium. "What about the dead bird?" he asked.

"Yes," Henri said, "somebody sent me a dead bird."

He explained that three such packages had been sent to Ottawa. One had been delivered to him at External Affairs; one had been addressed to the Department of Health and Welfare; and the third had gone to the Department of the Environment. The birds were all of the same species: red-eyed verios. They were all in the same condition at time of death: emaciated.

"They were in bad shape," Henri said, "but starving didn't kill them. We don't know what killed them, Neil. That's our problem."

"Where were the birds found?"

"The packages were mailed from Quebec."

"Is that their habitat?"

"They're migratory. They nest in Alaska and the Yukon, but migrate in late summer. One of the flyways is across Quebec."

"Are they diseased?"

"We don't know."

"Can't your biologists tell?"

"So far they haven't been able to identify the cause of death."

14

"It *might* be disease?"

"It might be; it certainly looks like it."

The waitress refilling their cups interrupted their conversation. Brody wasn't sure why Henri was involving him in a matter such as this. "What else kills birds?" he asked. "Chemicals?"

"Pesticides," Henri agreed. "Defoliants maybe; PCBs; heavy metals; aromatics."

"What do you want me to do?" Brody was honestly puzzled.

"Write me a report on biological warfare."

"I don't know anything about *that*."

"Yes, but you are very adaptive. Is that the word I want?"

"I guess so." Brody wasn't sure about the word 'adaptive'. He was sure about his own limitations. "Why don't you get a bright young graduate to do that for you?"

"Mmm . . . it's not quite as simple as you believe." Henri's expressive features reflected his concern. "My problem is this: I want to know as much as I can discreetly discover about American Army experiments with biological warfare substances."

Brody shrugged. "I don't think you'll get this kind of information in Ottawa."

"You think I need spies in the U.S. Army Chemical Corps?"

"Something like that," Brody agreed.

They shared a chuckle before Henri admitted: "I don't require much more than what is already known . . . and most of this can be gathered right here. Will you do it?"

"Okay," agreed Brody. But he had doubts.

"Good. I have an office set aside for you."

"Right, I'll start interviewing people tomorrow."

The emergency debate on Canada's dwindling future didn't excite much furor among the nation's legislators. When Brody took his seat in the Visitors' Gallery in the House of Commons that evening it was to find — he counted them — 36 members scattered across the government and opposition sides of the House. There were more concerned visitors than concerned MPs.

As he re-scanned the thinly populated forum below his heart leapt as he found Jan Stewart. She was seated three rows directly behind the acting prime minister. She was working diligently at some paperwork spread out on her desk.

Jan Stewart was in her mid-forties; slim, severe. The severeness was in manner, for she was patrician in looks. With no make-up other than the touch of lipstick, and wearing an expensive but unadorned pantsuit, she was a striking woman.

Thankful that she never glanced up, Brody pushed back in his seat nursing symptoms he thought belonged to persons much younger. It was several minutes before he succeeded in hearing any of the debate centred on saving Canada.

"I would like to address a supplementary question to the Minister of Indian Affairs and Northern Development concerning a fundamental abrogation of aboriginal rights in the matter of Quebec's secession from Confederation . . . "

The stentorian voice belonged to a distinguished-looking parliamentarian who was, when Brody located him, standing with thumbs hooked in his armpits.

" . . . In view of the do-nothing policies of this government and the crass neglect of the Minister of Indian Affairs and Northern Development who has so wilfully denied and abnegated the constitutional responsibility of the federal government . . . "

The silver-haired orator was interrupted by heckling and the banging of desk lids. Brody saw the Speaker of the House lean forward on his throne to speak directly into the microphone before him.

"Order, please," said the Speaker. "Does the honourable member wish to ask a supplementary question? He knows he cannot present an argument or enter into a debate."

A man sitting near the acting prime minister was on his feet. "On a question of privilege, Mister Speaker . . . " he tried.

"Order, please," said the Speaker. "The Chair will recognize the Minister on his question of privilege, but first the honourable member for Saanich will be recognized for the purpose of completing his supplementary question."

The Minister sat down, the orator on the opposite side of the centre aisle stood up and began again.

"I want to enquire of the Minister whether he and this government have any interest in protecting the rights of Indians and Inuit now residing in the northern hinterlands of Quebec, most of whom, I am told, prefer to be associated with the English-speaking elements of the soon-to-be-sundered, later-lamented, Canada."

He sat down to applause from his team mates, catcalls from the friends of the Minister on the other side. In all his years on the Territorial Council, Brody had never witnessed such juvenile antics. He leaned forward to hear the reply of the Minister of Indian Affairs and Northern Development.

"The honourable member for Saanich has implied that we do not have the interests of the Indians and Inuit at heart. I must protest that this is not the case and he cannot say that it is. In the matter of Quebec separating, the same rule will apply to the native peoples as to the English-speaking citizens: they may leave if they want to."

A storm of applause, boos, heckling and desk lid banging broke out below. Disgusted, Brody stood up to go. He was glad to see that Jan Stewart sat unperturbed and working as industriously as before.

The Department of the Environment was in Hull. Brody remembered Hull from his own days in the federal service back in the 1950s and '60s. It had been a grey cluster of industrial blight. Now the blight was gone, replaced by greenbelt landscaping and high-rise architecture.

He found David Scrimshaw — recipient of one of the dead birds — behind a maze of floor dividers and potted foliage. In his early thirties by Brody's guess, Scrimshaw wore a beard and a permanent look of surprise. He also looked tired. When he heard that Brody wanted to talk about the birds he insisted on taking him to the cafeteria.

As they stood in the elevator watching the floor signal lights blink on and off Scrimshaw said: "I can be more honest away from my desk."

The table Scrimshaw chose was against a wall. Brody felt comfortable enough with him to say: "You've got tea hanging there."

Scrimshaw absorbed the droplet with a paper napkin. "Beards ... nice to have, but sometimes messy." He smiled at Brody. "All right. The birds."

"What happened to them?"

Scrimshaw stared into his cup, put it down, dabbed the area near his mouth, then asked: "What killed them? Or what happened to them."

"What's the difference?"

"The difference," Scrimshaw said slowly, "is crucial. We don't know what killed them and we're not about to find out."

"Haven't you got tests?"

"We haven't got the birds."

Brody was puzzled. He'd been told that Scrimshaw, an ornithologist, was in charge of ascertaining the cause of death of the three birds. "Who's got them?" he asked.

"We don't know, and we can't find out."

"Where were they?"

"In our lab at the regional centre for wildlife studies. Our pathologists were running the tests."

"What happened?"

"They came and took them."

"Who did?"

"I said 'they', but the night security guard told us the next day they were Mounties."

"Did you call them?"

"I did." His smile was brief and bitter. "Before my boss could tell me not to."

"What did they say?"

"They denied it. At least they did initially. Then they changed their story and allowed that it 'might have been' their people."

"Jesus!" said Brody, his indignation rising. "Did you get to the guy in charge?"

"No." The bitter smile was back again. "My boss got a call from the Minister's Office."

"What would the Minister's Office have to do with it?" Brody asked.

"I assume somebody got to our Minister and told him to squelch discussion on the birds." Scrimshaw sighed, stroked his beard, then added: "You'll be convinced it's a biological warfare mistake when I tell you the guard said these 'Mounties' had American accents."

18

Brody thought about that. "Give me your opinion," he said at last. "What killed the birds . . . why were they stolen."

"I think they were victims of some man-made chemical — I don't know which — and, I haven't the faintest idea of why they were removed."

"What are your feelings about chemical-biological warfare?"

"Unconscionable."

The tables in the cafeteria began filling as government office workers congregated for the 10 o'clock coffee ritual. Since Scrimshaw was ignoring them, Brody continued with his questions. "Did you know the U.S. continues to test these substances?"

"I'm aware," Scrimshaw said. "But *I* can't do anything about it."

Brody had expected something different from the forthright man sitting across from him. "You don't care?" he asked.

"Mister Brody . . . I am an ornithologist. I love birds. I am involved in a losing struggle to save entire species of them. Do you know what I'm up against?"

"No."

"I work for a federal agency that claims responsibility for the preservation of birds and wildlife, but which hasn't the wherewithal to do so."

"Budget?"

"Right. In the face of ever-increasing pressures on both wildlife and habitat, the government cuts back on what's needed to combat it."

Brody nodded, taken aback by the vehemence in Scrimshaw's voice.

"We're understaffed . . . insufficient people . . . too many problems. Our normal programs are not getting done; all we do is respond to emergencies.

"You ask me to worry about the Americans and their god-damned nerve gas and endotoxin experiments. That's just so many more man-made hazards I have to try to cope with. I can't be specific in my hatreds, I just hate them all."

"Who?"

"The oil interests. The plastics industry. The pesticide lobby. The nuclear bomb testers. I hate them all."

The Department of Health and Welfare was housed in a tower overlooking the Ottawa River. Brody had come to see the third recipient of a dead bird, Sam Takeuchi. Sam was a squat and powerfully-built Japanese-Canadian.

The interview took place in a tiny conference room; four chairs bracketing a round coffee table. The room was otherwise bare. The one tall window afforded a view of the Gatineau Hills of Quebec across the broad Ottawa. Afternoon sun poured in unobstructed.

"Now," Takeuchi said, closing the door and sitting down, "you wanted to discuss what killed the birds in the first place. Right?" And as Brody's hopes rose he cancelled them with: "I have no opinions."

Brody was annoyed. "Why didn't you tell me that in the first place?"

Takeuchi ignored his question. "When I opened that box I said to myself: 'Sam, it's a bird. Your concern is people'."

"Is that *all?*"

"I was happy to send it over to Dave Scrimshaw at Environment."

Brody felt let down. "Well what about the implications? Aren't you concerned about what this might mean?"

Takeuchi sat like a Buddha disguised as a federal public servant. He shook his head. "I don't *want* to think of it."

"Don't you feel a responsibility?"

He'd struck a nerve, for Takeuchi abruptly leaned toward him one hand held palm upward. "I already have responsibility, for the health of twenty-five thousand Indians and Inuit."

"So?"

"I can't take care of *them.*"

Brody well knew the government had failed utterly in caring for the native northerners. But he wanted Takeuchi to tell him why.

"Why not?" Brody insisted.

"Well basically it's because they're committing suicide. They're doing it with alcohol."

"Okay," Brody said slowly. "I think that's correct. They won't take care of themselves."

Takeuchi seemed to feel better. Perhaps he sensed in Brody a common concern. "We've had epidemics up there, you know." He

20

said it in a confidential tone which surprised Brody, for epidemics in the North were common.

"I know," agreed Brody. "So what?"

Takeuchi regarded him for a moment, as if debating whether to go on. Then he said: "Tularaemia . . . Rabbit Fever."

Brody thought about that. Then he said slowly: "I lived there; I never heard of any Rabbit Fever."

"Remember the case — a few years back — of those Indian families, an entire settlement, that starved to death?"

"Jenkins Lake," Brody said. "Didn't they starve?"

"Tularaemia."

"They probably caught it from fur animals . . . " Brody started to conjecture.

"Muskrats."

"But no one dies from Rabbit Fever," Brody told Takeuchi. "Sick maybe, but . . . "

"This strain of Rabbit Fever killed twenty-four Indians."

Brody was shocked. "How did the government hide it?"

"Easy. The settlement was isolated; southerners are remote . . . and don't care anyway. We simply told the media twenty-four Indians starved to death . . . and hoped like hell the disease didn't show up somewhere else."

"Did it?"

"No. At least not that killing variety."

"That's good," said Brody, relieved.

Takeuchi didn't agree. "Did you ever notice the outbreaks?"

"Of Rabbit Fever?"

"Pneumonic plague in Indonesia; hoof and mouth in Eastern Europe; bubonic plague in Indo-China; tularaemia in Quebec."

"They've had Rabbit Fever cases in Quebec?"

"Quebec, spreading south into New England, west into eastern and northern Ontario."

"Anyone die?"

"Couple of old trappers. The rest responded to vaccines."

"Is Rabbit Fever endemic to these regions?"

"Yes and no. It used to be regarded as extremely rare."

Brody felt uneasy. "Where are these things originating?"

"You want *my* opinion?" Takeuchi pointed at himself. "U.S. Army experiments in Alaska."

"They suspended that testing site years ago."

Takeuchi looked at him. Then he shook his head.

"Alaska to Quebec?" Brody asked. "How did it spread?"

"We think it was migratory birds; they can carry the organisms in their faeces."

"How come," Brody's objection was earnest, "no one warns the public?"

"Sooner or later one of these problems will emerge as a catastrophe," Takeuchi said, tapping the sunlit edge of the table. "But until we're forced by events to admit it, the federal government will keep it secret."

That evening Brody mentioned one of the things about Ottawa that bothered him. "It's this secrecy, Henri," he said. "Everyone distrusts everyone else." They were walking along the footpath beside the canal.

"The wiretaps and things?"

"People are paranoid about them."

"I think they *should* be."

"Are phones in Ottawa really tapped?"

"Tapped and monitored. Have been for years."

"Offices?"

"Some of them."

"Yours?"

"Probably."

They walked past a group of Canada's unemployed who were sitting on and round a park bench. The non-workers glared at the two taxpayers.

"They look like they're waiting for the revolution to start," observed Brody.

"Twenty years too late," Henri replied.

They thought about that as they walked along the litter-strewn canal. The more Brody thought about the country, the more upset he became. "Where does the government get off at spying on people?" he demanded.

"It's a bad habit," Henri agreed quietly.

"When did it start?"

"When civil servants began leaking documents."

"They shouldn't," Brody said. "It's irresponsible."

"Well," said his friend, "the fault may lie on both sides."

"Don't keep me waiting."

"Who is keeping you waiting?"

"You are. I always have to ask you what you mean."

Henri smiled. "It's the trouble with you WASPs; I marvel that we put up with you as long as we did."

"Come on, Henri . . . "

"Where is the art of good conversation? You are all meat and potatoes talkers."

"Henri . . . "

"All right, my friend. The government fell into the bad habit of classifying every bit of information. The traditional elitist position: we-know-best. Some people in the Civil Service rebelled."

"Don't you think the people who stole the documents took an elitist position?"

"Mmm," said Henri approvingly. "That's not bad, for an Anglo." He glanced at his impatient friend and smiled. "So the government was wrong to classify so much information; but the civil servants who leaked the documents were also wrong."

"And that was the start of all this spying on people?"

"Just the start. From there we have followed the footsteps of our friends to the South."

"The C.I.A.?"

"You forget the Secret Service . . . and the F.B.I. Mister Hoover began it all so many years ago."

"Crap!" said Brody.

"In the States it is known as 'domestic espionage'."

"What does it do for them?"

"All kinds of things. They can assassinate a president; or a civil rights leader . . . or anyone who is gaining a populist following."

"Maybe that's just part and parcel of the republican form of government," Brody offered. He couldn't imagine the same bloody excesses in staid Canada.

"If the masses start believing in someone not of the elite . . . and if the elite is unable to discredit that person, buy him off, or otherwise neutralize his effect . . . he will be assassinated."

"Is that the way things are going to go in Canada? Do we have to copy *every* damn thing the Americans do?"

"Thus far in our history we have."

"This spying on people?"

"It will get worse. Did you know the Mounties could be recording every word you and I are saying this minute?"

"Out here? Do they *do* this sort of thing?" And when Henri didn't respond: "Why?"

"Well, like the Americans again, we plead 'national defence', or 'security'. But really it's just power.

"The problem of mankind, Neil. If one man can wield power over another . . . he will. Modern technology has allowed the Americans to wield power over much of the rest of the world and, despite their lofty moral ideals, they have killed millions, just to show that power."

"Sick."

"It *is* sick." Henri stopped on the walk to face him. "The question is: Can we avoid in Canada what has already happened in the States?"

"Well, it's only a problem, isn't it? I mean . . . every problem has a solution?" Brody's Law.

"Neil? Could anyone start a revolution without the authorities knowing?"

"I don't know." The thought had never occurred.

Henri started walking again. "Well think about it," he urged. His handsome face was set in a scowl.

"Okay," Brody started after him. "I can see your point."

"They have us documented, numbered, photographed and tagged."

"It's called 'social welfare', Henri."

"The government has equipped itself very well for spying on us."

Brody had to lengthen his stride to keep up. "Henri?" he said, looking at Henri's angry profile. "Are you sure you should be a diplomat?"

24

"Power is of little use if you can't control the people."

"Henri?"

"That's what power is all about."

"With your attitudes?"

"I'm merely educating you on why I'm going with Quebec."

"And you're also telling me why *I'm* going to New Zealand."

Chapter 2

Sunlight on the window shade lit the bedroom with soft yellow warmth and woke him. Brody reached for his watch on the bureau, startled to find a day so far advanced without him. It occurred, in the midst of shaving, that it was pre-dawn in Hay River.

On his way to find his new office at External Affairs, striding along the tree shaded streets of Ottawa, he had an odd experience. It was a crowd scene. A line-up of people on the sidewalk in front of a large residence. A police cruiser was parked at either end of the block. Two officers stood, leaning their backsides against the far car, chatting.

Puzzled by the absence of placards at a picket line he headed for it.

"End of the line!" someone called as he approached.

"What's happening?" Brody asked a sandy-haired man in his mid-thirties.

"Free food from China," the man said with the faintest of ironical smiles. "If you want a package you'll have to line up."

All Brody could manage was: "Food packages?"

The man's ingenuous expression didn't change as he said: "Ten minutes from now we get the propaganda broadcast . . . then they hand out the food."

"What broadcast?" Brody asked.

"See those loudspeakers?" The iron horns hung from the corners of the brick building before them. "Tape recorded speeches." Brody winced, visibly, and the man laughed at him. "Not as bad as you'd think."

"Chinese communist propaganda?" Brody challenged.

The people in the line-up crowded closer to listen.

The man was unabashed. "I thought that too," he said easily.

"All that running dogs of capitalism stuff. But you know? Listen to what they're saying — and realize what you have here . . . " he waved a hand to indicate the crowd, " . . . all these educated un-employeds — and suddenly mister, you start to realize that the Chinese have something to say to us."

Brody was shocked. "You believe that communist propaganda?"

"They aren't starving in China; they are in Canada."

"They aren't starving in Canada!" Brody protested.

"Close to it, Mac," offered someone in the crowd.

"Welfare can't keep up with inflation," said someone else.

"No unemployment insurance for professionals."

"You ever try raising a family on welfare?"

Brody couldn't reply to all these interjections so he stood in the warm morning sunlight and addressed the lot of them. "These food packages are a communist propaganda exercise; an attempt to gain points over capitalism. Can't you *see* that?"

The silence of the crowd was hostile. Brody turned to the man he'd approached in the first place. "Don't *you* see that?"

"You're wrong," the man said flatly. "There's no propaganda benefits. No one knows about it."

"Well! They're sure as hell going to find out!" Brody sputtered. "Just wait until the news media hear about this. It'll be on every TV screen and newspaper front page in the country."

A chorus of hollow laughter went up at this. Brody looked at the sandy-haired man again, for an explanation.

"The Chinese Embassy has been distributing food packages for months. The news media are just *not* interested." He glanced at his watch, then back at Brody. His smile was quizzical. "You staying for the speeches?"

Brody said no. He left, anxious to talk to Henri about his startling discovery of a bread line at the Chinese Embassy.

The security guard in the entrance hall of the External Affairs building asked Brody to wait while he called Henri's office. When he hung up he said: "You'll have to wait until his secretary comes down for you."

Brody had time to examine an exhibit in the lobby. It was a glass tower filled with old shoes. Small spotlights — one at each corner — illuminated the jumble of wrecked footwear. It reminded Brody of something he'd seen in Germany right after the war: a revolting display of the personal effects of gas oven victims.

"Mister Brody?" A short, well-dressed woman about his own age held out her hand in greeting. "I'm Lucille Parent, Mister Robillard's secretary." Her eyes crinkled at the corners when she smiled.

Brody liked her at once. "What's this?" he asked, pointing at the shoes.

"Do you like it?"

"Well, no."

"It's art," Lucille said, strolling around it like a tourist.

Brody followed her, viewing a second time the eight-foot-high mountain of castoff shoes: leather shoes, bright coloured plastic shoes, high and low heeled shoes. All the shoes were worn out, run over, broken down. Compared to its contents the glass and brass container of the refuse looked elegant.

"This is *art?*" Brody asked.

"Fifty-five thousand dollars worth," Lucille said, "not counting the case. It's called 'Shoes'."

"Oh," said Brody.

Lucille went to the guards' glassed-in enclosure to negotiate Brody in. As he signed the book she told the guard: "Mister Brody will go for his security clearance this afternoon. Until he gets his card, please let him in on our temporary pass."

The guard reminded her that Brody would need a new pass every day. "Only good for twenty-four hours," he said.

On the way up in the elevator Brody remarked on the remarkable security.

"The odd thing about it," she told him, "is that all the locks and bars and procedures and personal security checks aren't directed at spies at all; they're aimed at our own employees."

Brody didn't pursue it.

"By the way," Lucille said as they walked down a broadloomed corridor, "Mister Robillard can't see you this morning. He asked me to show you your desk, and I've laid out the background materials he has for you."

Out of the corridor now they worked their way through a maze of coloured floor dividers and potted plants. In the labyrinth were civil servants. They were reading at their desks, talking on the phone, or visiting over the dividers.

"Here's your office."

"Do I rate an office?"

"Mister Robillard insisted on it," she said. "I put everything I thought you'd need in the desk; if you need anything else, I sit over there."

Brody thanked her and added, as she was leaving: "Will you tell Henri I'm here?"

"Sure . . . and by the way, Mister Robillard would like you to join him in his office," she pointed across the room, "for a sandwich at noon hour."

Henri was pleased to have his company.

"Sit down," he said, indicating a coffee table surrounded by deep chairs. At the far end of the room was his desk.

"This your office or a living room?" Brody growled.

"Oh-oh," murmured Henri, loosening his tie for comfort as he sat down. "I think I hear the voice of a taxpayer."

Brody told him of the scene at the Chinese Embassy. His indignation returned with the telling. From start to finish Henri sat observing him.

"It's a disgrace," Brody concluded. "It should be stopped."

"We can't very well stop it, Neil. If the Chinese Embassy wishes to distribute food to the needy, it's their business."

"But it's a national disgrace!"

"Yes," Henri smiled at him. "You said that."

"It's a propaganda exercise."

"You mentioned that, too."

"Well?" demanded Brody. "Isn't it?"

Henri, who was classifiable as a genuine 'senior government official', looked unimpressed and uninvolved. "What the men in the line told you is correct, Neil. The news media have not played this story up."

"But why? Are they afraid of the government?"

"No. I don't think that is so. But coverage here would be free publicity for the Chinese. The media owners are capitalists too, you know."

"So they practice self-censorship?"

Henri smiled fondly at him. "Don't be so hard on the media, Neil. They've always practiced self-censorship."

Lucille came in with their sandwiches and milk. They paid her, and thanked her, and Brody said: "When does he bring you *your* lunch?"

She laughed. "Often. He's the kindest boss in Ottawa."

When she had gone Henri protested: "Because of the splendour of my surroundings — of which you disapprove — you think that I am insensitive to my subordinates."

"I didn't say that."

"You made your point . . . years ago. I remember you taking sandwiches and tea to the aircraft maintenance crews. Even on the days following the raids when you were exhausted."

"The groundcrew were exhausted too," Brody said. "They wouldn't sleep the night of a raid, then they had to stay up all day repairing the aircraft."

"Right," agreed Henri. "But you remained the only squadron commander in the war, either side I'm sure, who regularly served tea to the groundcrew erks."

They laughed at the word 'erks'. Neither had heard it in years.

"It was the sandwiches," Brody said. "The lunches going down to the hangar line were plain bread with a slab of cheese. Ugh!"

"You could have told the messing sergeant to improve them," Henri pointed out.

"Look . . . " Brody grew enthused, remembering it. "I inspired entire kitchen staffs!"

It was a warm moment, interrupted by Lucille who knocked on the door, then opened it. "Don't forget you have an appointment."

"Is he here?"

"Yes."

Henri sighed and looked disappointed.

Brody stood up, gathering the paper plates and sandwich wrappings as he did so. Henri collected their milk cartons and led the way to his waste basket.

"Did you get that list of people to contact?" Henri asked, then added as they strolled toward the door: "I urge you to be as patient as possible with these people. You may even be asked why External Affairs is meddling in a scientific area."

"What will I say?"

"Tell them the truth. You are doing a crash study, but for general information only." Henri smiled thinly. "That way their precious scientific knowledge isn't threatened."

"Hurt feelings?"

Henri nodded. "Yes. They will wonder why we didn't form another inter-departmental committee."

"A task force?" Brody suggested with mock innocence. He recalled his years in Ottawa.

"Or a task force," Henri sighed. He paused at the door, hand resting on the knob. "I want you to remember that the subject you are reporting on has implications that go far beyond any of the people you will be dealing with." His dark eyes were intent. "All right, my friend?"

Brody nodded. "I hope I can get the information you want."

Henri turned the door knob but before opening it said earnestly: "It's not the information I want, so much as your thoughts on the matter." And before Brody could reply he added: "I regard you as an original thinker. Your thoughts are important to me."

Henri swung the door open, laid his hand on Brody's shoulder in a farewell gesture. "Five-thirty," he said. "I'm usually ready to leave about then."

By the time Brody returned from the fingerprinting and polaroid posing ceremony, it was 3 p.m. Lucille had thoughtfully included phone numbers with the list of names of people he should contact. He started dialling. His phone was out of order.

"What's the matter with it?" Lucille asked, her voice filled with concern. "Is it dead?"

"No. It seems to dial okay, but I can't get a reply from any of the numbers you gave me."

She looked at her watch, then brightened. "Well of course not. It's three-fifteen. No one back from coffee break yet."

Sure enough, by 3 : 30 he was talking to people.

"Is this the Defence Research Board?" he asked, unable to understand the barrage of French that opened the conversation.

"Yes, this is Doctor Macklin's office. Can I help you?"

"I'd like to talk to him, please."

"I'm sorry, Doctor Macklin is attending a conference in Miami. He won't be back until next week. Can anyone else help you?"

"No," said Brody. "Uh . . . I'll call him next Monday."

"He won't be in Monday."

"He won't?"

"No. He missed one day of his weekend, so he'll be taking Monday."

"Can I call him Tuesday?"

"Yes."

"Thank you."

"You're welcome."

He wrote 'Tues' beside Dr. Macklin's name and then tried another.

"Hello?" he said, when the jumble of French subsided. "Is this General Orbach's office?"

"Yes, sir. Can I help you?" It was a man's voice.

"I'd like to speak to the General; is he in?"

"Who is calling, please?"

"Ah . . . he doesn't know me."

"Are you sure you have to speak to General Orbach? Could I refer you to one of our public information officers? Captain Johnson, at six oh-five-five-oh, would be pleased to respond to your enquiry. If your query is in French, Major Darriault, at the same number."

"It isn't an enquiry and I do wish to speak to the General," Brody said.

"Right, sir. Could I have your name, rank and organization?"

"Telephone number?" Brody asked sarcastically.

"Yes, sir. Telephone number and reason for call."

"Surely that's between the General and myself."

"If you feel that way, sir, may I suggest a letter? Address it to

Brigadier-General O-for-Orlando Orbach comma, National Defence Headquarters, Ottawa, postal code Kilo-one-Alpha, Oscar-Hotel-three. Got that?"

Brody's temper required a moment to control. Finally he said: "Do I take it that you are not going to connect me with General Orbach?"

"Can't do it, sir," said the cheerful voice, "until you let me fill out my form here."

"My name is Brody; I am with External Affairs. The number here is four, nine six four six. I wish to arrange a meeting with the General."

"About what, sir?"

"About biological warfare." Brody's voice was taut with anger. "Now, is he in?"

"No sir."

"Jesus!"

"The General is at Fort Benning, Georgia, on a counter-insurgency course."

"How long will he be away?"

"Another week."

"Leave my name on his desk. Ask him to call me when he gets back."

Brody, still annoyed, called the next number on the list. It was a French name, so he anticipated an outburst of French when the secretary answered.

"Privy Council Office," said the girl's voice.

Faint with surprise Brody asked to speak to the Assistant-Secretary to the Cabinet, (External Affairs and Defence), Mr. Yvon Degair.

"I'm sorry. Mister Degair is on language training."

"When will he be back?"

"Next month."

"Who is taking his place?"

"No one."

"Who should I talk to?"

"About what?"

"Biological warfare."

There was a pause. Then: "Maybe you should take this right to the top."

"Who, top?" Brody was thinking of the prime minister.

"Joel Reid-Wilkinson."

Brody recalled the intense intellectual — prematurely bald and aggressively officious — he'd known years before in Ottawa. "What's *his* title," Brody asked.

"Deputy Secretary to the Cabinet, Operations. Do you want his number?"

He tried the number. Reid-Wilkinson was at a meeting.

"I didn't get to talk to one of them," he reported to Henri as they left the nearly deserted building.

"Perhaps not to worry, Neil. There are reasons."

They walked across expanses of grass, under trees, heading for the nearby Rideau River and the path that paralleled it.

"Meetings!" Brody complained. "Conferences. Senior officials — a year at a time! — away on language training."

"Mmm," mused Henri.

"Who does the work?" Brody wanted to know.

"Nobody does."

Brody was disgusted. "Come on, Henri. I'm serious."

The sun was behind them; it was shirt-sleeve weather. Accordingly they removed their jackets.

"All right," agreed Henri, "I'll tell you. No one stays in their offices because they haven't enough to do. So they attend meetings. They attend each other's meetings. And they go to conferences." He regarded his tall companion, then added: "Most people in Ottawa are looking for jobs."

"Do they think Canada is about to fold up just because Quebec is leaving?"

"The blame for the break-up lies with Ottawa. It's unlikely the provinces will want to continue with the Confederation arrangement."

"Surely these people could catch on with the provincial governments," Brody said.

"The jobs might be there," Henri told him, "but the money

34

wouldn't be. Also, there is the matter of work. Most people in Ottawa are totally unfit for work."

"What's going to happen, Henri? Where's this all going to wind up?"

Henri looked at him, then interrupted their walk by heading for a park bench which overlooked the river. They sat down, stretching their legs.

"Union with the United States will be my final gift to the English-Canadians," Henri said.

"Is *that* what your discussions with the U.S. Embassy are all about?" Brody demanded. Then: "Most English-Canadians don't want any part of it."

Henri's laugh was brief. "What the people want has nothing to do with it. The power brokers on your side of the country want peaceful union."

"Will they get it?"

"If the U.S. wants it."

"Can you see any advantages, Henri? Anything?"

"For your people? Or the power structure."

"For Canadians generally."

"Absolutely none. With union you become depressed areas of the United States; without union, one of the under-developed countries."

"Christ," said Brody.

"The wealthy of Canada feel their wealth would be safer in formal union with the States," Henri observed in a matter of fact tone.

In the outer office where Brody waited was a brass plaque. 'Brig. Gen. Orlando Orbach, B.Sc., C.D., Director-General, Land Offence and Defence'.

"Okay, sir," said the young clerk. "You can go in now."

Brody opened the door and stepped into a small auditorium, a conference room, the General's office. At the far end of an oval-shaped conference table, framed by a crescent of full-sized NATO flags, was General Orbach.

"Wing Commander Brody!" the man said, standing up and advancing on him. The General was chunky yet trim; his muscles

35

were under a healthy layer of fat. Without the heavy rank epaulettes hanging on the corners of his pale green shirt, he'd have been moon-faced Civil Service with a shorter haircut.

"I'm proud to make your acquaintance, sir!" Genuine enthusiasm lit the General's brown eyes as he gripped Brody's elbow with his left hand, pump-handling with his right.

The General was guiding him to a chair at the huge table, still talking. "What a stir you caused round here! Everybody that remembers World War Two has a Brody-story. You are, did you know it? . . . famous."

"No," said Brody, wondering if he could run not walk to the nearest exit. "I never think of the war."

"Well, you should!" The General sat down beside him. His expression was one of eagerness and concern. "Did you know that not one World War Two experienced man is still in service?"

"I'm not surprised," said Brody quietly. "It was a long time ago."

"But look at you. You look as if you could walk out and start up a Liberator right now. Fly it on a raid over Germany."

"Lancasters," Brody corrected him. "The Lib's were used in other theatres." He tried changing the topic. "Are you ready to be interviewed?"

"No! I want to talk about the War." The General paused, looked momentarily embarrassed, then asked: "Why do you wear your hair that long?"

Brody's hand reached for the back of his neck, as if making sure the auburn hair still covered his nape. Under it was angry red scar tissue, the result of an aviation gas fire that followed a crash. "You mean it's not military," he said lightly.

"Well, no. It hasn't even been civvy style for years."

"I let it grow right after the war," Brody said with finality.

The General nodded, accepting the odd fact. "At noon hour — after I've given you my briefing — my friends and I wondered if you'd have lunch with us; afterward tell us about your wartime experiences."

"Good God, no!" It came out more emphatically than he would have wished.

36

In the awkward moment that followed, Brody was aware that he'd hurt the General's feelings.

"Okay, sir," said the General sadly. The use of 'sir' was strictly complimentary; a true indication of the respect Brody's war record engendered in a non-combat general. "It really is sad, you know."

"What is sad?"

"They say you have never attended one Bomber Command reunion. Not one."

"Well . . . " Brody didn't know what to say.

"No one has even talked with you about your experiences."

"There's nothing to talk about," Brody said firmly.

"All right," the General capitulated suddenly but with a sigh. "Before I start my briefing, would you like me to outline my military background?"

Brody did not want any such thing.

"Good. Well, I'm an Army man. Joined right out of university. Automatic commission, of course; went with the degree . . . not like in your day, ha, ha."

The General watched to see if Brody laughed. When he didn't, he continued: "Nothing really happened to me until Paul Potter. Great man that!" The General tapped Brody with an unwelcome finger. "I idolized him."

"You did?" Brody could not help saying. "The Minister of Defence?"

"His ideas! Integrate the forces. Out with the admirals! Out with the rusty-dusty generals; the dogma; the tradition. Get rid of it!" The General's eyes glowed. "Replace it with good, practical, Harvard School of Business Management techniques."

Brody found himself eye to eye with the General. He was expected to say something. He said anything. "What did you do?"

"I said to hell with tradition. To hell with the idea that military officers shouldn't be political activists. I got out on the stump!"

"For Potter?"

"For his principles. I averaged thirteen speeches a week."

"Didn't your commanding officer object?"

"Him?" The General's voice held withering contempt. Then his face brightened. "I had the pleasure of firing him myself, two years later."

"What happened? I mean, as a result of your speeches on behalf of the Minister."

"I was jump-promoted from captain to full colonel within the year."

Brody was appalled. "When," he asked, "did you make it to brigadier?"

"After Potter left, it was tough. I didn't get the promotion for five years."

"Congratulations, nevertheless," Brody murmured.

"Thank you. Now, are you ready for my briefing?"

"Yes." Brody was glad they were getting down to it at last.

"I'll brief you right from here . . . there's only the two of us. Hell, I guess I can't." He stood up. "My controls are up front. But you stay right here; swing your chair when it's time, to see the screen over there."

As he headed for the front of the room and the pulpit with its bouquet of microphones, Brody looked at the opaque glass which was, apparently, a rear-projection screen.

"Can you hear me?" asked the General from the podium. "Can you hear me? Test . . . ?" The volume came up as he adjusted things. "Testing . . . testing. How's that?"

"It's fine, General. I can hear you without the mike. Can we get on with it?"

"Soldiers and civilians are working together with improved team spirit these days at Canada's Defence Headquarters in Ottawa . . . " started General Orbach. And he went on to say that the present strength of 150,000 people hardly compared to the 787,000 in uniform during WW II. He was into the breakdown of service population by organization command structure when Brody interrupted him.

"General!" Brody had to shout to gain his attention. "What I really wanted to discuss is biological warfare."

"Offensive, or defensive? I wear two caps in this job."

Due to the distance separating them they were speaking loudly.

38

The General snapped off the mike and returned to the table. This time he chose to sit across from Brody.

"I'm just trying to find out what our role in this area is," Brody told him.

"Certainly," said the General. "What is it you'd like to hear?" He looked earnestly interested in Brody's problem.

"What's happening in CBW. State of the art; who is doing what."

The General stood up. "I have just the thing for you," he said. "I'll have the corporal screen it for us."

It was a talk. Immortalized on 16 mm film, one camera only, full face, so as not to confuse the actor who was a straight-teeth-crooked-smile U.S. Army colonel. He never smiled once.

> The U.S. Defense Department spends three billion dollars each
> year on a vital deterrent and a standby weapons system. It is
> known as our chemical and biological warfare program.
> Government sponsored research and development projects to
> produce and protect against germ and gas warfare agents are
> underway on at least ninety-two campuses . . . with the emphasis
> on protection.
> Scores of private firms — ranging from industrial giants to small
> engineering firms — are also involved.
> Ten military bases serve as centers for the research, testing and
> storing of chemical and biological munitions.
> Although much of the work we do is top secret, it is permissible
> to state that the United States has assured means of delivering
> biological and chemical munitions to enemy soil.
> Harmless germs and gases have been successfully test delivered
> by guided missiles, bombs, artillery shells, hand grenades and
> aerosol sprays.
> Using low flying airplanes as delivery vehicles, the aerosol
> sprays are considered the most effective.
> More than half the total research and development budget is
> spent for defensive purposes. Our scientists are working hard to
> develop vaccines, antibiotics, and chemical and electrical warning
> systems capable of alerting the nation to a surprise chemical-
> biological warfare attack.
> Your Department of Defense cannot overlook the possibility of
> a surprise attack which could be launched with less effort, less
> expenditure, and with greater accuracy than the attack on Pearl
> Harbor.

Many other countries are known to be experimenting with germ and gas warfare.

Some of our noted authorities believe the Soviet Union is at least as far advanced as is the United States in CBW work.

It is always possible that the civilian — not the military population — might be the prime target.

If an enemy were attacking the New York-New Jersey coastal area, he would be more interested in producing disability in the millions of industrial workers there than in the few thousand military personnel stationed in the target area.

More research is necessary. It is needed to assure the security of our country against surprise attack or to minimize surprise. In that regard, every university and every citizen has a patriotic obligation to contribute.

The picture faded into a wind-ruffling Stars and Stripes and an unseen military band played loudly. Brody was glad when the lights came up. Thus far, the morning had been a bust. He knew he would have to ask specific questions.

"General . . . aren't we involved here in a chemical and biological arms race?"

The General's affability faded. The eagerness left his eyes as he warily considered Brody's question. "I don't see that."

"A paving of the way toward progressive escalation to the use of increasingly deadly weapons? Weapons that could be lethal to entire populations?"

The General, his moon-face set in lines of senior officer disapproval, placed his hand, palm down, on the table before him. "I'm surprised," he said, "to hear you take this line. What you're saying is: 'War is bad; ergo, weapons are bad'. It's a sentimental argument, and I'm disappointed that a man of your known accomplishments in Area Bombing would take such a position."

If the General was surprised at Brody's position, Brody was even more surprised to be classed as a mass-murderer during the war.

"Conventional bombing . . . " Brody started to say.

"In the present admittedly faulty world sociological pattern, war is still a fact of life. We must be prepared to deal with it realistically."

Brody realized that the General's rounded exterior was misleading; that the eyes were not soft and brown . . . they were hard agate.

40

It flashed through his mind that this was the man who'd been in Fort Benning, Georgia, the week before learning how to control 'insurgents' in Canada.

"Conventional high explosives . . . " Brody started again.

"The amount of damage a nation will execute on civilians is not determined by its weapons. It is, rather, defined by the philosophy of the nation using the weapons."

"But germ warfare! . . . " Brody sputtered.

"There is no 'nice' way to fight a war, Mister Brody."

"Have you seen the Minister of Research and Development yet?" Henri asked him as they left the External Affairs building.

Ottawa was hot and steamy again so they took off their jackets.

"What about?" asked Brody.

"CBW."

"I've got a call in for André Dallaire."

The path along the Rideau was thronged with office workers and lounging unemployeds. Every shade tree and park bench was in use.

"His boss is Jan Stewart." Henri's smile appeared innocent. "I thought you might prefer to interview her."

"Why?"

Henri glanced at him. "Beautiful woman; single." And when Brody failed to answer: "Weren't the two of you together on the barricades?"

Brody's anti-Vietnam War activities had resulted in the loss of his Ottawa government job; his resignation on point of principle. Jan Stewart had led the anti-war movement in Toronto.

"Should I go ask her to marry me?" Brody's voice was sharp.

"Oh my no." Henri held his hands out, pushing, in mock-Gallic horror. "Not *that* woman."

Brody was instantly curious. "What's wrong with her?"

"Cold!" Henri shivered. He huffed and puffed and generally overdid it. "A terrible tongue. She *carves* opposition members."

"Sounds formidable," Brody agreed, his thoughts as firmly on Jan as they had been since he'd arrived back in Ottawa. "How come she isn't married?"

"She hates men."

Chapter 3

"Neil Brody!" Joel Reid-Wilkinson, 'mandarin', stood in the open doorway beaming at him. He was elderly but fit; like a health food endorsement. His remaining hair, now white, wreathed a wrinkle-free dome. Behind steel-rimmed glasses were eyes like blue marbles. "Come in, Neil," he said cordially. "Come in, come in."

They shook hands at the entrance. Reid-Wilkinson's office was even larger than Henri's. Not only did it have the furniture in a conversation-pit setting, but a boardroom table and the lounge on which he napped.

"Sit down. Tell me about yourself. How have you been?"

The warmth of the welcome was genuine. Reid-Wilkinson had been an Intelligence Officer during the war. Brody recalled the wooden tables lined with I.O.s waiting for the crews to return from the raids. The questions; the forms. He'd always treated Brody as old comrade-in-arms.

"I'm fine," Brody said, wanting to get the visit over with. "And you?"

"This report you're working on for Robillard," Reid-Wilkinson smiled, "how long will it take you?"

"It's a three month contract. Why?"

"How would you like to come work for me?"

Brody could not have been more surprised. He had worked on task forces and committees with Reid-Wilkinson years ago, but he'd thought the disgrace of his anti-war activities in the 1960s would still be in effect. The look on his face evoked a chuckle from his host.

"It's all right," Reid-Wilkinson said, leaning back, crucifixion style, both arms along the back of the divan. "I know who I'm talking to."

"You do?"

"Oh, sure, you're a radical. But I figure that Robillard and I are the only two people in Ottawa who appreciate what you really are: an original thinker."

"Oh?" Brody couldn't recall any of his original thoughts enshrined in Ottawa.

"Your high-speed data transmission net: voice, computer data, documents *and* photos. You were ten years ahead of your time."

Brody's broadband microwave system had boosted the government's coast-to-coast communications capability from 1,000 words a minute to 100,000 and opened the way for transmitting and recalling different kinds of data.

Reid-Wilkinson continued: "And people like me don't forget that DFC and two bars of yours. They didn't hand *those* out with the rations."

Noting Brody's discomfort he went on: "And as for you being a radical, well . . . if anyone says anything I can point out that you were right: Vietnam *was* a mistake."

Brody nodded slowly. Vietnam. Three million dead. A chemical-polluted, devastated little have-not country was now just 'a mistake'.

"You have a communications problem?" he asked.

"Yes." Reid-Wilkinson came off the cross to lean over the table at him. "But we'll come to it when I show you the Crisis Centre."

Brody was about to ask if the Centre was concerned with CBW but Reid-Wilkinson seemed to be on to something else.

"I wish Yvon were here," he said.

"Who?"

"Yvon Degair . . . the man in charge of our Crisis Centre."

Brody remembered the name. "On language training isn't he?"

He wasn't prepared for the laugh he got with that one.

"Ho-ho," Reid-Wilkinson chortled. He wiped an imaginary tear. "Yvon is one of the architects of the Quebec Revolution. His French is pure joual."

Brody was puzzled. "He's taking *English* language training?"

"No, of course not. His English — while not good — is perfectly understandable."

"Then . . .?"

"He spends his time in Quebec City."

"For the Privy Council Office?"

"No. For the Quebec government. He's a future cabinet minister."

"Oh?" Brody was mystified. He asked a northerner's question. "Who's paying him?"

"We are."

"Why?"

"Well," Reid-Wilkinson became both serious and confidential, "because it's in the interests of the federal government to do so."

"You said he was a revolutionary."

"A famous one!" Reid-Wilkinson looked surprised that Brody didn't know. "Yvon Degair? You don't remember?"

Brody didn't remember, so Reid-Wilkinson told him.

Yvon Degair was a fiery campus radical of the late 1960s. According to Reid-Wilkinson, a "natural leader of young people." Like many such, Degair was fated to graduate. Suitable employment not offering itself, Degair continued as a separatiste activist.

"He had an extraordinary talent with bombs," said Reid-Wilkinson. "He really did."

One of his bombs killed three cleaning ladies instead of the Royal Bank president, and Degair drew 30 months for manslaughter . . . plus the other charges which included sedition, assault, seditious conspiracy, counselling to kidnap and murder, and three contempt of court citations.

"They say he was marvellous in the courtroom," Reid-Wilkinson said with a chuckle. "Alternately screaming and spitting at the judge, shrieking threats at the witnesses. Quite something I'm told."

"Did he go to jail?" Brody asked.

"No. His lawyer filed an immediate appeal."

"Did he ever go to jail?"

"No. He works for the Privy Council Office."

Brody knew that the conversation was a bad one for someone like himself. But he couldn't stop. "May I ask why?"

"Well under the new federal law aimed at freeing more accused persons — with or without bail, and in Yvon's case without — we thought we should hire him."

Brody tried to imagine what someone with Degair's title of

Assistant-Secretary to the Cabinet (Foreign Affairs and Defence) might make. $26,000? $36,000?

"We had him on the payroll when his book came out in translation."

"Book?" asked Brody, his thoughts elsewhere.

"A blockbuster for Canada. Titled: *Maudits Anglais!*"

"I never heard of it," Brody said.

"You wouldn't have, if you lived west of Ontario."

Brody was glad, in that instant, that he was not going to meet Degair. "Why did you put him in charge of the Crisis Centre?" he asked.

"Most people think of it in terms of natural disasters, ecological emergencies, nuclear runaways. In fact, the government set it up to deal with civil disorders, insurrection, riots." Reid-Wilkinson's smile was bright but his cold blue eyes were watching for Brody's reaction.

Brody was appalled at what the man was saying but he was determined not to let on. "Bombings?" he asked.

"Yes! And that's why we hired Degair."

"Hire an expert," Brody said, deadpan.

"Right. And a good investment it's been."

"It has?"

"Certainly. Look at how well this whole Quebec move to independence is proceeding."

"Pretty smoothly," Brody agreed, carefully.

Reid-Wilkinson glowed. "Under our bilingual program these past years we've trained a group of competent French-Canadians in the art of self-government. People like Henri Robillard."

Bull*shit*, Brody thought. Henri had told him of the struggle he'd had making his way through the Civil Service in the days when bilingualism was a handicap.

" . . . result in a political transition that will have a spirit of co-operation rather than antagonism," Reid-Wilkinson concluded.

Brody looked at him in amazement. The man was serious.

Reid-Wilkinson leaned ahead in his chair, an evangelical look replacing the craftiness in his eyes. "Our task — my task — is to provide the government with plans for the peaceful turnover of power, first to Quebec, then to the United States."

Brody was disgusted.

"We have to protect the wealth!" the mandarin concluded vehemently.

Brody, his anger growing, didn't want to continue the conversation. "Are you going to show me the Crisis Centre?" he asked.

The Crisis Centre was a complex of three rooms. The outer two offices had pastel walls, beige broadloom, and ceiling to floor drapes. The furniture looked as if it had never been used. What was in use — and what dominated the two rooms — was communications equipment: radios, and automated print read-out machines.

Brody followed Reid-Wilkinson into the third room which was dark. As Brody's eyes became accustomed to the dimness he made out desks, a boardroom table, a raised dais counter which overlooked the room. Along the opposite wall, at ceiling height, were TV monitor screens.

"This is our operations room," Reid-Wilkinson said with pride.

"Who runs it?"

"There's a man here twenty-four hours a day, seven days a week . . . never a time when the Centre isn't manned."

The expense was an affront to Brody. He couldn't recall one of the 'civil disorders, insurrection and riots' that Reid-Wilkinson claimed was the reason for the Centre. "You have people come in when an 'emergency' occurs?"

"That's right." Reid-Wilkinson left him to circle the counter. "Watch this, Neil."

The entire wall under the TV monitor screens became an illuminated outline map of Canada.

"Cities over a million . . . " Small blue lights winked on here and there, mostly in Ontario, Brody noted.

" . . . over one hundred thousand . . . " Yellow lights twinkled.

" . . . fifty thousand population." And amber lights speckled Canada.

The coloured lights were extinguished then, leaving the map outlined in pale white light.

"In case you wondered," Reid-Wilkinson said from the controls, "we have our military bases." Green lights winked on across the land. There weren't very many.

"Is that all the military bases we have?" Brody asked.

"Yes. For the sake of efficiency the bulk of our armed forces are right here in Ottawa."

"Do these bases you're showing me represent fighting forces?"

Reid-Wilkinson laughed. "None of our armed forces 'fight'," he said. "That's not what they're set up to do."

"Then what are these bases for?" Brody felt uneasy about Canada's non-violent defence forces.

"Regional disparities. You can see by their location — scattered across Canada — they're all in poverty areas. The payroll is important to the local economy."

"There's no military significance then . . . ?"

"No. Just a means of redistributing the money."

"Still," objected Brody, "they must represent something. Otherwise why have them here on your board?"

"I assure you: they are of no earthly use."

"Maritime patrol?"

"Useless," said Reid-Wilkinson emphatically. "Look . . . " and he illuminated the blue and yellow lights. "You can see how far removed from possible trouble they are."

" 'Trouble' is in the cities?"

"The only place where trouble can be." He turned off all the map lights and took Brody out of the operations room. "What do you think of it?"

Brody was only mildly impressed. He wanted to ask what the Crisis Centre would do about a biological warfare attack, but he felt it was the wrong question.

"What are all those TV screens for?"

"Oh . . . they connect us with everywhere. We can talk to people at Defence Headquarters here in Ottawa; our embassy in Washington; the Pentagon, of course; and the CIA command operations centre in Langley, West Virginia."

Brody's hackles rose.

"We can provide ourselves with TV coverage of civil disorders as they happen," Reid-Wilkinson continued.

"*What* civil disorders?" Brody asked, his irritation showing. "Canadians will never fight . . . never protest."

"Well they might!" Reid-Wilkinson insisted. "That's why we arranged the Civil Unrest Act."

His choice of words intrigued Brody. To prolong the conversation he sat on an empty desk and said: "Tell me about that legislation."

As the apparent author of the bill, Reid-Wilkinson seemed happy to tell Brody about it. "Events in the States . . . suppression of the blacks and everything . . . convinced me we shouldn't become complacent up here."

The violence against minority groups in the U.S., thought Brody, made Canada's problems look like sandbox squabbles. "What did you do?" he asked.

"To provide the 'background' necessary for this kind of thing, I had Yvon help the police set off bombs."

Brody tried to look impressed. "How many were enough?" he asked coolly.

"Fifteen; and no one got hurt."

The idea of preparing public opinion by such methods repelled Brody. Still, he wanted to know why.

"I've always marvelled at the complete passivity of Canadians," Brody said. "They seem endlessly capable of accepting almost any degree of harassment from government . . . "

"What *kind* of harassment?" Reid-Wilkinson interrupted. His voice was hard.

Brody played innocent. "I mean everything," he said, "from income tax forms to parking meter fines. Canadians always just seem to accept these things."

"Oh." Reid-Wilkinson was relieved. "Yes. Well that isn't what the Civil Unrest Act is all about. We needed some enabling legislation to permit this, for instance." His gesture indicated the Crisis Centre.

"You were telling me you could watch a riot on TV, right from here."

"As long as we know in advance of the riot."

"Why do you have to know in advance?"

Reid-Wilkinson's icy eyes shone with enthusiasm. "So we can position the cameras. If necessary we can rely on the port-a-pack units carried by the police."

"Police?" Brody wondered where they came in.

"The Mounties. I forgot to mention that one of those screens is 'M' Division Civil Unrest headquarters here in Ottawa."

"Do the Mounties help you run the Crisis Centre?"

"Yes. Between them and Defence Headquarters."

"What did you want *me* to do?"

"Neil." Reid-Wilkinson's voice adopted an intensely personal tone. "Have you any idea of what's happened to 'information' since you left Ottawa?"

"No, I guess not."

"Information — the ability to collect it, store it, retrieve it — has become the sine qua non of national security."

Brody nodded. "Foreign espionage . . . " he started to agree.

"No, Neil! It's a matter of *internal* controls."

"What?"

"Not foreign spies; our own internal power structure is in jeopardy."

"I don't understand," Brody admitted.

Reid-Wilkinson gestured at the blank row of TV screens in the next room. "Both the Mounties, and Defence, are stockpiling information . . . keeping it from each other and, more importantly, from me."

Brody wondered what kind of information he was talking about.

"The Privy Council Office must not be by-passed in this way, Neil . . . I've decided to set up my own intelligence gathering organization."

"What do you want *me* to do?"

"Take charge of it. I'll hire you on contract to do something else, but what I want is either: a tap into what Defence and the Mounties are up to, or a revolutionary new method of gathering our own information." Reid-Wilkinson was talking so fast saliva was collecting at the corners of his mouth. "Will you think about it?"

Brody wanted no part of an internal spy network but decided not to tell Reid-Wilkinson. "I've got this report to do for Henri Robillard."

"Afterward?"

"I was planning to go to New Zealand."

"Oh." Reid-Wilkinson was disappointed. "Well if you change your mind, let me know. Can I show you the rest of my operation?" he asked.

"Before we go," Brody asked, "what is the role of the Crisis Centre in times of disaster?"

"Such as?"

"Epidemics, say."

"That would be Health and Welfare."

"What if it were a livestock disease?" Brody asked, thinking of CBW agents such as anthrax that attacked man through domestic animals.

"Agriculture," said Reid-Wilkinson. "They have responsibility there."

"Chemical spills?"

"Usually localized, which makes it a provincial matter. But at the federal level we'd have Environment; Northern Development, maybe; and Transport . . . since spills usually happen during transit." Reid-Wilkinson was heading for the door. "Let us out?" he addressed the hidden microphone and TV monitor lens.

The steel door swung open at a press of the guard's button. They paused outside the door while the guard marked down their time of exit. They were back in the office world of the Privy Council.

"Isn't there a lot of overlap in responsibilities?" Brody asked. "All those departments?"

"That . . . " Reid-Wilkinson held up a finger to mark his point, "was what prevented the Centre from fulfilling one of its two major intended roles."

"Which were?"

"Civil Disaster, and Civil Disorder."

"Civil Defence?"

"Oh my no. There isn't any of that. We wouldn't *want* any of that."

"If there was it would probably come under National Defence," Brody suggested, nursing the conversation along.

"Yes . . . I'd think perhaps it would. But the phrase 'Civil Defence' worries me." He looked at Brody. There was worry in those marble eyes. "Would you like to see the rest of my operation?"

As they strolled along a comfortably furnished corridor, Reid-Wilkinson unburdened himself. "What you were saying about the overlapping of departmental responsibilities is a prime headache for the PCO. Have you any *idea?*" He stopped walking to confront his visitor.

"No; no I haven't."

"Not to bore you, but: in addition to inter-departmental rivalries we have the dispute with Treasury Board. We have federal-provincial considerations. Political priorities . . . what I sometimes call the 'porkbarrel imperatives' . . . ha ha ha."

Brody failed to laugh.

Reid-Wilkinson didn't notice. "Bilingual priorities, U.S. government pressures and, of course, the needs of business and industry." He added, as an afterthought: "We've always had to help business and industry."

They started walking again. Brody wondered where they were going.

"At the moment we have two major tasks: preparations for Quebec independence; and, effecting union with the United States."

"The States?" Brody prompted.

"Working with Robillard you're abreast of *that* situation, but I'd like to point out the years of work already put into it over here."

"Years?"

"The integration of the two economies wasn't accomplished overnight."

"The Continental Energy Plan?"

"Yes. The Canada-U.S. Continental Energy and Water Plan Agreement. That was the start."

Brody recalled a lot of people in Canada thinking differently at the time. "Start?" he said.

"Yes. It represented a far more efficient allocation of Canadian resources. It laid the foundation, I like to think, for full economic union with the States."

Reid-Wilkinson led him into an office, past several desks into a back office. A black steel door defied the mandarin.

"Madelaine!" he called.

"She's not here," someone called back.

"Will you go find her to open the vault?"

While they waited Reid-Wilkinson continued about Canada and the U.S. His enthusiasm was undisguised. "Canadian factories will have the advantages of large-scale production, as well as access to the huge consumer markets of the States."

Brody checked the impulse to argue. Instead, he asked about progress of the grand plan.

"We're almost to economic union now. Subject to a few more concessions from us, Washington is coming round. We'll have our Free Trade Area."

"Removal of tariffs?"

"Right. From there it'll be downhill sledding. Ah! Madelaine. Would you open the door for us?"

And while she worked on the combination, he continued talking to Brody. "We'll see a blending of our two countries' fiscal and social policies. We already have common institutions for dealing with pollution and social unrest. Next we'll have common securities regulations, common anti-trust laws and, why not? . . . a common currency."

"Full union?"

"Of course! Common citizenship." The vault door opened. "Thank you Madelaine, thank you!" he enthused. "Come here, Neil."

The walk-in vault was about seven feet square. It was lined with shelves on which were stacked — floor to ceiling, all three walls — reports.

"Reports, Neil! We've been commissioning these studies for years. Academics have grown wealthy churning this stuff out."

Brody was astonished. "Have you read all these?" he asked.

"Heavens, no. Too much. But it's all here." He walked closer to a stack and began reading titles: " 'U.S. Education Practices'; 'Free Enterprise Medicine, the Practice of'; 'Election of Law Enforcement Officials in the Democratic State'; 'Military Funding of Social Research'; 'Toppling of Sovereign Governments by Democratic Business Interests, Attitudes toward'."

As they left the vault Reid-Wilkinson asked: "What do you think of *that* for a resource?"

"Impressive," murmured Brody.

"I've budgetted three million in similar research for this year." A worried look creased his bland face. "And none too soon, either."

"I didn't know so much had been done," Brody said truthfully.

Encouraged, Reid-Wilkinson continued: "I chair four major task forces myself. I call it my 'key sector' approach. Financial institutions, transportation, communication, and energy."

"Our government has a pretty big stake in all these things, right?" Brody led him on.

"Right! The problem is to get them all turned over to private enterprise . . . the banks, the airline, the CBC." Reid-Wilkinson started for the door. He seemed glad of the chance to show Brody around.

Down the hall he paused at a door, opened it. Brody glimpsed a small room with half a dozen people working at desks. "What is this?" Reid-Wilkinson asked.

"Education," answered a voice.

"Thank you." He shut the door and turned to Brody. "Didn't want to interrupt, but you could see what they are: a task force."

"On education?"

"Yes. All kinds of interesting questions." He started walking again. "Things such as the integration of black students into Canadian schools."

"Blacks?"

"We anticipate an influx of blacks; they think Canadians don't discriminate."

But they do, thought Brody, and they will . . . just as soon as they get enough blacks to discriminate against.

Reid-Wilkinson opened another door, looked in, then closed it again. "Business." He started off again, Brody following. "Teaching Canadian businessmen such things as the art of creative lobbying."

Bribes, thought Brody.

"And the Puritan work ethic, and the maximized dollar," Reid-Wilkinson added. "Canadians are notoriously lazy, you know."

As they continued walking he pointed to another door. "They have a tough one in there . . . how to deal with English-Canadian fanatics."

"What are those?" Brody found it difficult to imagine one.

"Oh, I guess you'd call them the loyalists of our time."

"What are they loyal to?"

"You know ... the idea of an independent Canada." Reid-Wilkinson shook his head. "Totally out of touch."

Before Brody could ask what the task force was proposing — his own sympathies lying with the 'fanatics' — they were back in the ante-room to Reid-Wilkinson's office.

"The men from the ad agency are in your office," his secretary said. "They asked if they could go in and set up their 'dog and pony show'."

"Is *that* what they called it?" Reid-Wilkinson laughed. He turned to Brody. "That's Mike Patterson for you." And when Brody failed to respond he explained: "Patterson, Snivelly and Wright, the Toronto ad agency that ran the entire campaign for the Liberals last time around."

"Oh?" said Brody.

"The Prime Minister ... " Reid-Wilkinson's voice dropped to a conspiratorial whisper and Brody had to lean to hear, " ... wants to award Mike with an Order of Canada medal."

"What for?"

"For his selfless contribution to the Party."

"An ad agency?"

"Sssh! Yes." Reid-Wilkinson was so close Brody could count the hairs growing out of the freckles on the top of his head. "Do you know that Patterson *gave* the services of his agency to the P.M.'s campaign? Only charged the Party for the cabinet ministers and back-benchers."

"What about Liberal candidates?"

"Those too." Reid-Wilkinson stood back, smiling. "I'll have to get in there. I've asked them to outline a media campaign to start the education of Canadians on the glories — advantages, anyway — of the American way of life."

"By the way," said Brody, remembering, "I left my briefcase in your office."

Reid-Wilkinson asked his secretary to get it.

"Oh, I forgot to tell you about my sub-committees." He walked to a file cabinet, opened a drawer and read off some titles.

" 'Disposition of Civil Servants, federal', see also: 'Employability of Canadian Civil Servants in U.S. Government Agencies'; 'Disposition of Musical Ride, Mounties'; 'Disposition of Parliament Buildings'; 'Disposition of War of 1812 Monuments and Historic Markers'."

He turned to Brody, hand outstretched. "You can see, Neil, we do have a heavy responsibility."

Brody managed to congratulate him on his efforts for Canada.

The halls of Parliament are sort of hoary and hallowed, once you get wandering in them. Brody found himself walking more quietly than he might had he asked for an office number and directions. As it was, he felt stealthy.

'The Honourable Jan Stewart, Minister of Research and Development' said the brass plaque on the polished door. It was unlocked so he walked in. There was a girl at the reception desk.

"Is the Minister in?"

"Have you an appointment?" the girl counter-questioned, looking at the appointment book beside her.

"No I haven't." He sat down in a visitor's chair. "But if you'll tell her an old friend would like to see her, I'll wait."

The girl was smiling when she returned from the inner office. "If your name is Neil Brody, please go in."

The inner office was small; the furniture old; and the room had no window. Jan had left her desk and was walking toward him. She looks marvellous, he thought.

"Neil!" She cupped his face in her hands and kissed him. The kiss was part social, part old-comrade, but part erotic too.

"Where have you been all week?" she asked, stepping back to look at him. "One phone call to say you're in Ottawa, then nothing. Is that the way you treat old friends?"

He felt himself sinking into her compelling eyes. "I'm sorry."

"You ran away to the Northwest Territories; you've been divorced for years . . . and not a word from you . . . what's a girl to do?"

Brody glanced round the panelled office. "You haven't done badly."

"Thank you." She extended a hand and led him to the antique sofa.

"Did you buy this?" Brody asked.

"Good heavens, no! It belongs to the office."

"It looks like Sir Wilfred Laurier might have used it," he observed.

"What are your plans now?" she asked.

"New Zealand."

Jan didn't like his answer. "Still running," she said.

"I . . ."

Her hand went to his cheek. "Neil," she said, "I'm sorry I said it."

"It's okay . . . I guess I did run . . . "

"From me?"

Brody didn't know what to say. They continued looking into each other's eyes. Finally he confessed: "I was never certain whether you cared as much for me, as I . . . " he stumbled over saying it. "I mean . . . I was married; and you were single."

Again she touched his cheek. "I know," she said softly. "I knew it then. You were — and are! — so honourable." Her smile was mischievous. "It was so old-fashioned, Neil . . . *we're* so old-fashioned!"

The Chief of Science Programs, Defence Research Board had — as far as Brody could see — every electronic gadget ever devised for an office. A miniature TV, an AM-FM radio, double dictation equipment, recorder for phone calls, speaker-phone, digital desk calculator.

Behind the oversize desk, palisaded with stacked documents, was a beefy little man just now bent over a letter. He was immaculate. Heavy horn-rimmed glasses were imbedded in rosy flesh, the stems disappearing into a silvery grey pompadour.

Brody had time to look round the room. One wall was a royal purple backdrop for certificates. A lifetime of courses. The diplomas went from ceiling to knee height.

"Mister Brody?" The soft and pink Dr. Macklin was standing.

"Doctor Macklin?" Brody made no motion to shake hands. "May I sit down?" He sat.

"Yes," said Macklin, uncertain for the second. "Please do."

"I won't take much of your time . . . " Brody started to say.

"I dialogued with my National Defence counterpart, Brigadier Orbach," said Macklin. "He tells me you are outspoken . . . even abrupt." He smiled benignly at Brody and then re-perched on his leather chair.

"I'm putting together a summary of Canada's role in biological warfare research," Brody said.

"This for External Affairs?"

"Yes. Henri Robillard."

"Surely," Macklin rocked back in his chair, pudgy fingers laced over a straining vest, "Henri is aware of the inter-facing of our inter-departmental committees."

"He asked me to do it."

"Oh." Macklin rocked ahead again. The fussy little fingers began re-arranging papers on his desk. He looked up at Brody again, his eyes opaqued by the thick lenses. "If it will provide greater equanimity between departments, I'd be pleased to speak to the question."

They sat looking at one another. Brody suddenly realized he was supposed to say something. "What is Canada's role in biological warfare research?" he repeated.

"In summary it can be said that as a signatory of the Geneva Protocol of 1925, Canada is pledged to refrain from the offensive use of chemical and biological weapons."

"What about 'defensive' use?" Brody asked.

"That's a very meaningful question." Macklin cleared his throat and started again. "I might state that Canada, as signatory, is morally bound to the terms of the agreement which, of course, do not prohibit signatories from keeping up with the state of the art and insuring their defences."

"Have we got these weapons or not?"

"As I believe I began to state earlier, Canada has observed this agreement sincerely, and its armed forces do not have in their arsenals or stockpiles any munitions charged with toxic material, either biological or chemical." Dr. Macklin sat looking at him.

Brody tried to offset the pain he was sitting on by concentrating anew on the answers to his questions. "*What* is being done?"

"Speaking to the present arrangement now it may be said there is an established Canadian research and development program in the military applications of biological and chemical operations, but the program is designed specifically to deal with the defensive and protective aspects of the possible use of such agents by hostile forces against Canada."

"What program?" Brody asked, squirming.

Macklin looked hurt. "The point has been registered but before any feedback is possible . . . "

"The program!" Brody exclaimed.

"I just wanted to reiterate," Macklin said unctuously, "that the feedback should be directed back to the originator of the observation."

"For Christ's sake," marvelled Brody at the double talk.

"The rationale is to speed up the on-site initiation of effective protective procedures, devices, equipment, therapeutic agents, vaccines, and symptom identification kits for the Canadian armed forces."

"Is *that* what the Defence Research Board does? What about Suffield?"

"Yes," said Macklin, settling back and re-lacing his fingers. "If you look at the picture which is all part of the package you will find the establishment at Suffield was set up — when the need surfaced — as a joint British and Canadian facility to test and evaluate military chemical stores and equipment."

"What do they *do* there?"

"We have expertise on site for proving the protective equipment and material proposed, researched, and developed at D.R.E."

"D.R.E.?"

"Defence Research Establishment."

"What about the U.S.?"

Macklin looked serene. "We dialogue trans-border."

"Isn't there a formal agreement?" Brody asked, knowing full well there was.

"We exchange feedback."

"With the United States *and* Great Britain?" Brody persisted.

"I would have to respond to that affirmatively."

"Who else?"

"Australia."

"Why?" Brody asked, wondering if any of this was worth it.

"The dialogue initiated in time-frames between our four countries is very meaningful in terms of observation feedback."

"What!?" Brody exploded.

"In summary," Macklin continued blandly. "I would reiterate in response that the Technical Cooperation Program endeavours to improve the combined efficiencies of these four countries and to minimize duplication of effort."

"Oh for Christ's sake," breathed Brody. Then: "Is Suffield not an open air laboratory for the other three countries?"

Macklin looked at his watch, then again at the outraged Brody. "I think I can state unequivocally that at Suffield it has been possible to disseminate simulant biological materials and innocuous particles, record and measure their behaviour during downwind travel in open air." Macklin stood up and smiled. "I'm late for a meeting."

The taxi ride from the External Affairs building to the airport took about half an hour.

"Just give me the major points," Henri told him.

"I didn't learn anything original. You probably know all this."

"That's okay. As I told you, I'm interested in your thoughts on this matter."

"Dirty matter," Brody amended.

The taxi ran a yellow light. Henri leaned ahead to speak through the wire cage separating driver from passengers. "There's no hurry, take your time." The driver nodded.

"I'll give you the facts first," Brody said, "my thoughts afterward."

As they drove along the canal driveway past groups of unemployeds, Brody told him about the birds. "Nobody seems to know what killed them. The two guys I trust the most — Scrimshaw and Takeuchi — said it *could* be pollution."

"Air pollution?"

"A contributing factor. But they were thinking of man-made chemicals."

"But the pathologist doing the autopsy didn't discover any of these things," Henri reminded him.

"Well, neither of these guys thought CBW agents were necessarily the cause of death. They didn't rule it out, mind you," Brody added.

"Did anyone have any suggestions as to who stole them?"

"The Mounties, apparently. Or at least guys dressed like Mounties."

"Okay," said Henri. "I don't think there's much to be gained worrying about what became of them. I'd still like to know the cause of death." He turned to Brody. "Have you any thoughts on that?"

The taxi was passing Carleton University. A nearby administration building was being picketed by students. The only sign printed large enough to be read at their distance said: GET THE COPS OFF CAMPUS!

"What's that all about?" Brody asked.

"Since the Quebec decision to separate, the Mounties have been infiltrating the student movement."

"What 'student movement'?" Brody asked.

"The Canada First Movement," Henri told him, "just one of many student groups that have formed recently. Over at Ottawa U it's the Canada Unity Movement."

"Oh," said Brody, peering over his shoulder at the picket line until it disappeared from view. He was wondering if the students might form the vanguard of the rebellion it would take to save Canada.

"We're almost to the airport, are you going to give me your thoughts?"

"Okay," said Brody. "First, I think you should realize that chemical-biological warfare has been under development for the past thirty years."

"Yes?"

Brody looked at him. "A lot of people think the idea of using germs to kill animals and people — and plants too — is far fetched. Too crude.

"In the early days that might have been the case. But Henri,

60

they've got some very sophisticated substances. Germs genetically engineered to resist known antidotes."

"Ugh!" Henri pulled a face.

"That's right. We all say 'Ugh', and then forget about them. Who wants to think about these things?"

"You sound angry."

"When I think about it, I get angry."

"Good. Give me more of your angry thoughts."

"Because of its proximity to us, we usually think only of the United States in connection with biological warfare."

"But there are other countries, I know that."

"What I started to say is that almost any country — developed or developing — can afford to manufacture biological agents. Even research their own. As a weapon it's cheap."

"As a weapon I'd think it unreliable."

"The unreliable factor is secondary, in my opinion, to the cheapness factor. They are easy to produce, easy to deliver, easy to keep secret."

"There must be factors against it."

Their conversation was drowned in the sudden, rising shriek of jet engines. The noise increased to a thunder as the jetliner, at full takeoff power, roared by 500 feet over their heads.

When the noise had passed, Brody hurried on with the points he wished to make. "The things against biological warfare are the common sense things. The germs you use to attack someone may turn round and attack your own people."

"That's what I was thinking," Henri said, satisfied that his point had been upheld.

"It's a mass weapon," Brody continued, "uncontrollable as to its specific targets. That is, it could be friend or enemy. It could be a world suicide weapon."

"The old doomsday machine of science fiction in the fifties. Right, Neil?"

"I always thought 'doomsday' machines were nuclear."

"Mmm," Henri mused, looking at the manicured golf course they were passing, then: "Maybe you're right. I'm sorry for the interruption." He turned to Brody again. "Give me the rest of it."

"Two thoughts; that's all I have. You ready?"

Henri nodded.

"One: Canada has absolutely no defence against chemical or biological attack. But neither has the U.S."

"Has anyone?"

"No. They talk about vaccination programs and automatic warning systems, but as far as I can make out, there is absolutely no defence against either type of warfare."

The taxi was pulling up to the terminal. Brody hurried to finish. "Two: our noble allies — the Americans — carry on their own research and development programs without sharing the results with us, the Australians, or the Brits."

Henri checked his bag at the counter, then consulted his watch. "Five minutes," he said happily. "Is there anything else to tell me?"

"There probably is, but I can't think of it. I'll put it all in my report."

They were interrupted by the public address system. A girl's voice, speaking French, announced the flight to Quebec City. When she paused before repeating it in English, Henri smiled at Brody. "Isn't that a heavenly sound? Rimouski."

"What Rimouski?"

"Her accent. I'd recognize it anywhere." He held out his hand. "See you next week."

Chapter 4

Brody came to. About to throw up he gripped the edge of the bunk and rolled out of it. The concrete floor was cold through his thin socks.

Stomach churning he felt his way along a panelling of steel bars to the opposite wall . . . and along the wall to a sink. His leg bumped porcelain and he'd found the seatless toilet. Brody dropped to his knees, embracing the clammy bowl.

When he awakened again he was still on his knees, arms across the toilet, his forehead braced on his arm. The stench of his own vomit rose from the bowl and caused him to retch and heave again. The effort exhausted him. His throat burned and he longed for a drink of water. He slept, dreaming of water.

Sunlit darkling water, sailboats on the Ottawa.

As Jan turned onto the Parkway Brody asked: "How far to Eganville?"

"Hundred miles."

"Does Pete know we're coming?"

"He has no phone . . . it'll be a surprise."

Pete Ranallo had been active in the protest movement with them; the visit was for old times' sake.

"Pete taught biology at U of T, didn't he?"

"Until he got caught in the purge."

"Didn't anyone think of the U.S. teachers as a resource?"

Jan glanced at him, smiled, shook her head. "The winds of nationalism were howling through Canada."

Brody didn't reply. He was content to be with her. More than content: he was deeply happy. Looking at her now in profile, she seemed as youthful as when he'd first met her.

She'd been his reverie during the droning monotony of aerial survey; thousands of hours in *The Queen* tracking invisible grid lines on the sub-Arctic land mass. Jan — the dream of her — had seen him through that long Arctic night pinned in the wreckage and alone.

"Why did you do it, Neil?" She asked the question without looking at him.

He knew what she meant. Why had he let the years go by? He knew he loved her, had loved her, would love her. The lump in his throat made talking difficult. "I don't know," he managed at last.

"You didn't take your wife to the Territories . . ." a note of bitterness was in her voice, " . . . why didn't you ask me?"

The question was familiar: he'd put it to himself ten thousand times. "I was much older than you, Jan . . . I'd been married twenty years . . . "

"Did your wife accuse you of lusting after younger women?" Jan's look was cool and amused. "Me?"

Her observation was so correct it hurt. His reaction had been to suspend his feelings. Now, reunited with her, self-denial seemed less than noble. Even stupid.

"Sorry, Neil." Her hand left the wheel to compassionately pat his thigh.

An erotic thrill surged through him. "God, woman! Don't *do* that," he cautioned her.

"Why?" A bridge, a truck, and a curve in the road took her hand and attention.

"Do you know what you do to me?"

"Oh?" She risked a teasing glance. "A fellow sufferer?"

Brody found himself asking a far too personal question.

"Have you had any . . . love affairs?"

Her foot came off the accelerator; as the car slowed she said: "Neil . . . I don't know whether our friendship will ever go that far but if it does . . . " she looked at him full face, affection for him lighting up her eyes, " . . . don't expect to find me a trembling virgin."

They were laughing as Jan stepped on the gas again. In the miles that followed they filled in the missing years. Brody told her about Lin Lee, *The Queen*, flying in the North. She told him of the frustrations of being a social worker in Toronto. Her blue eyes lit with indignation at the memory.

"I realized after years of trying to get city politicians to do more than complain publicly about 'greedy people on welfare', that society isn't interested in solving the problems of poverty."

"So you went into politics?"

"Out of sheer frustration."

"How did you choose a party?"

"The only candidacy I found open, I applied for."

"And you got it?" Brody was astonished.

"No one else wanted it."

"You won the election?"

"Not that year. But it gave me a claim to financial and organizational backing from the party for the next election."

"Good for you."

They stopped at the post office in Eganville to ask directions. All three employees gathered at the counter to help him.

"Ranallo?" The ruddy faced postal clerk turned to his colleagues. "Ranallo runs the ecology school, doesn't he?"

They gave him directions, telling him to look for a renovated schoolhouse.

The gravel road leading north was narrow and wound between cedar and brush-covered hills. The farm fences were split log, or combinations of piled rocks and cedar rails, the butt ends lashed together with rusted wire. The farms, Brody could see, were cash deficient.

'Ecology School'. The sign was a birch slab with the letters burned into it. Beside it was a mailbox with two names painted on the side. 'Ranallo' was the second name.

Brody opened the wide gate, waited for Jan to drive through, then closed it. The sandy road led into a shady cavern of 15-foot cedars. Beyond the cedars they found a weathered, red brick farmhouse, a dog and, across the way, a reclaimed one room schoolhouse.

The dog stopped barking as the owner of the place emerged from the house.

Pete was slight but wiry; a jawline beard framed a narrow face and accented sensitive brown eyes. The beard, his curly dark hair and the slim straight nose gave him the look of a Roman aristocrat.

"Pete!" Jan said, kissing and hugging him.

"You two finally got together, did you?" Pete asked, happy to see them. "Come in . . . I want you to meet Karen."

Karen Knudsen was a beautiful girl in her late twenties. She was deeply tanned and the hand she extended in greeting was strong. "Pete has often mentioned you both. You're up there on his list of great Canadians."

The kitchen was large, but there seemed less than enough furniture. There was a circular oak table, a sideboard and a wood burning stove. Karen moved the kettle to the hot side. "I'll make tea," she said as she joined the others at the table.

"Were you one of Pete's students?" Jan asked her.

"Yes." The look she gave Pete was unabashed love. "He was a great teacher . . . still is."

"That was in the States?" Brody asked, puzzled by her American accent.

"No . . . I was a social worker . . . in Chicago." Karen said 'Chicago' as if it were special somehow. She turned to Jan, her voice filled with interest. "You were a social worker."

Despite the contrast in appearance — Jan with shoulder length dark hair and Karen with her blonde hair tied back — the two women were similar. It was, Brody realized, their animated way of talking. Meeting each other for the first time they reacted like favourite sisters.

"I'm a failed social worker," Jan told the younger woman. "I got into politics to escape."

Jan's laconic remark drew a laugh, but Karen was deeply interested in Jan's career. "Were you able to do more for the poor once you were a member of parliament?"

Jan shook her head. "As an MP — particularly as a new MP, and a woman at that — I was totally helpless to effect any change whatever."

"Yes, but they made you a cabinet minister." Karen's statement of fact was a question.

"I'm there as the Token Woman," Jan said lightly. "When the government decided to co-opt the Women's Liberation Movement, they needed a token woman to elevate to Cabinet status. They chose me."

In the momentary silence the sound of the furiously boiling kettle seemed loud. Pete reached back and removed it to the cooler area of the stove.

Karen continued questioning Jan. "But aren't you in better position now? To help; to inspire women by your success?"

Jan reached across to touch Karen's arm. "Women must realize that domination by males hasn't changed one jot."

"But can't you help? As a cabinet minister?"

Jan sighed. Regret was in her eyes and voice as she explained it. Brody realized it was something to which Jan had given a lot of thought.

"Being in politics isolates you; you find yourself making endless decisions on what you think is valid evidence but which — when you examine it closely — turns out to be personal bias, or advice given you by people with vested interests."

She went on to tell them that being a minister only increased the isolation; and that inability to effect changes, or to carry through programs she knew to be important, led to crises of frustration.

"You have to form alliances with other politicians; and this means compromises which, ultimately, water down the good effects you'd hoped for with your own programs."

Then, before Karen could ask another question, Jan altered the sombre mood of the kitchen by closing the discussion. "Tell me how you met Pete . . . I'm interested."

"I decided to leave Chicago," Karen said, "I was doing graduate work at Toronto in Pete's last year there." She went to the sideboard for cups.

"Does your Ecology School make a living for you, Pete?" Brody asked.

Pete nodded. "The local school board pays me twenty bucks a class; and I teach four of them per week. The Board buses them here."

"Eighty dollars a week?"

Pete laughed. "It's not university salary."

"But he loves it," Karen said. "And he spends as many hours

preparing for his ten-year-olds as he did when he taught at university." She poured the water into the teapot.

"Do you miss the university?" Jan asked Pete.

"No, I don't think so. I got awfully tired of fighting the system; of trying to inspire others to fight. I once thought that if people understood the problems...they would make the necessary changes," Pete said earnestly.

"It never works out, does it," Jan observed.

Pete agreed with her. "The belief that understanding will stir Canada — or any other country — into action, is fallacy."

Once the conversation swung to Canada it stayed there.

"It's the social problems that are destroying this country," Karen said at one point, her face flushed with emotion. "Unemployment, urban decay, crime... " She thought for a second. "Poverty, housing, hunger.

"I was a social worker. I studied. And I worked. And I tell you that for all these problems... I've heard, or read, hundreds of solutions."

"You're talking about changes to society?" Pete asked.

"The forms, Pete. The structures: tax law amendments; giveaway programs; subsidies for this group or that. Welfare insurance!" she said with contempt.

"You're against welfare?" Brody asked.

"I'm against welfare substituted for social reform."

Jan and Brody left soon afterward, promising to return again. Outside the gate, parked beside the 'Ecology' sign, was a police cruiser.

"Let me see your social identity cards," the Mountie ordered.

They talked about it during their early evening drive back to Ottawa.

"He not only *checked* our identities," Brody complained, "he wrote down our names. What the hell for?"

"I guess they want to know who visits Pete."

"What business is it of theirs?"

"Pete's a known radical."

Brody pursed his lips in irritation. Finally he said: "Remember

68

what Karen said about the solution to our problems lying with the people?"

"She was talking about the social problems."

"I agree with it," Brody said, looking at summertime Ottawa Valley going by his window.

Jan was silent for a few minutes, and when she spoke again her voice was altered. "You realize, don't you, that what you and Karen are saying is deeply radical?"

" 'The solution lies with the people' is radical?" Brody asked in disbelief.

"Yes, Neil . . . and very dangerous."

"Why?"

"Because society fears the radical." She glanced across at him, fondness in her eyes. "The person who believes in humankind. That's you. You're saying that Canadians could solve their own problems."

"Canada's problems," Brody amended.

"Precisely! And that's *radical*."

"All right," Brody agreed slowly. "I'm a man who believes in people. I believe in the worth of the individual. I believe . . . " he hesitated, unaccustomed to expressing these thoughts, "in the morality of mankind."

"Society has good reason to fear you."

"Why?"

"Every shaky step ever made toward democracy and equality has been made because of people like you."

"Okay," Brody agreed, "maybe you're right."

"Society favours the status quo," Jan persisted. "The radical threatens to change things. If people begin to believe in that person, he or she suddenly becomes dangerous."

Brody thought about it as they drove. Finally, and without mentioning it to Jan, he came to a decision: he'd look for a leader . . . someone willing to save Canada. If he couldn't find that person, he would try himself.

It was noon hour in Ottawa on a sunny September day; civil servants were leaving their office buildings to enjoy it. Those located downtown went people watching on the Mall; those who worked in the office complexes on the city's outskirts went for walks in the greenbelt.

As Brody and Henri left the External Affairs building with their sandwiches and milk cartons Brody lodged a complaint. "I never see you any more; you're always in Washington."

The warm sun filtered through the maple trees touching, here and there, a recumbent civil servant. There were no vacant benches.

"How about under that tree?" Brody suggested.

They settled on the grass, their backs against the corrugated bark.

"I like nature and all that," Brody said during the sandwich unveiling, "but how come, if you only have a few minutes, we aren't eating in your office?"

"My friend: I can monitor my own statements . . . " he glanced sidelong at Brody, "but not yours."

Brody made a face. "Have you any proof your office is bugged?"

"Mmm, no. But when they built this place — it's fairly new you can see — I assume they put in the necessary wiring to bug all the offices."

"No wonder you're heading out."

"Vive Quebec," Henri said with feeling.

It reminded Brody of his report. He told Henri: "By the end of next week Lucille can have it for typing."

Henri nodded as he pried open his milk carton. "Tell me a little something to brighten my noon hour."

"You want to hear about the 'biologicals' part of Chemical and Biological Warfare?"

Henri was sorry he'd asked. "Tell me about germ warfare," he sighed, "but briefly."

"Our military seem to believe that Canada is not suitable for biological attack. Atomic weapons would be used instead."

"Three large cities?"

Brody nodded. "The military," he hesitated, "I can't differentiate between the U.S. and our own . . . look at CBW as just another item in the arsenal."

Henri's expressive eyebrows went up. " 'Use it when you need it, General'? Is that the attitude?"

"They much prefer chemical weapons."

70

"Good reason," Henri said. "They can control and predict with chemical agents."

"Oh." Brody thought of something else. "About immunization against biological agents. Did you know that radiation destroys immunity?"

"No," Henri admitted. "I didn't."

"It makes a first strike with nuclears, followed by a second strike with biologicals, the best way to use the weapon."

They were silent a moment, then Henri asked: "Do you think anyone in the world would ever use these things, Neil?"

"Well . . . given the fact that these weapons are here, now, ready to use by most military forces in the world . . . I'd have to say, yes."

Henri sighed. "It makes Canada's problems seem insignificant, doesn't it."

"Which reminds me," Brody said, "I'm doing some research of my own."

"On what?"

"The Constitutional Crisis."

"Good. Will you get angry?"

"Why should I get angry?"

"If you get angry you might be moved to do something."

Brody told him of his intention to look for a leader. Someone willing to lead English-Canada out of the mess it seemed to be heading into.

"What about yourself?"

Brody hesitated. "I got away from the problems," he said at last, referring to his years in the Territories. "I'm unknown. I think it has to be some public figure . . . someone . . . " He let the thought trail off.

"Someone more aggressive than yourself?"

"I can be 'aggressive'," Brody said firmly. "But I don't think much of my qualifications."

"If you can't find a leader," Henri persisted, "will you do the leading yourself?"

Brody nodded, then changed the subject by asking Henri about his annexation talks in Washington. "Can you tell me?" he asked.

"I'm now arguing the continentalization inevitability theme."

Brody groaned. His diplomat friend smiled at his distress. "You'll be glad to hear that my negotiations are not going well."

"But why?" It never ceased to amaze Brody that Washington would not covet a treasure such as Canada.

"The U.S. has generations of brutalized, bred-to-compete people to draw on; they don't need Canadians." He wadded the sandwich wrapping into the empty milk carton, then added: "The U.S. could supply Canada with every form and type of leader we might need: managers; teachers; foremen."

"We haven't got the qualifications for U.S. citizenship?"

Henri shook his head. "The colonial mentality of English-Canadians, passive — coupled with the high education standards, and their expectations for an easy life — make them unsuitable candidates for U.S. citizenship."

"Is that the truth, Henri?"

"The truth, my friend."

The office of Robert F. Jordan was less ostentatious than Brody might have anticipated. The room seemed dark, the furniture was old-fashioned, the walls wood panelled. Beyond the drapes were, presumably, windows . . . as well as the downtown Toronto traffic.

"Good of you to come see me, Mister Brody," said the large and confident president of the Canadian Manufacturers Association.

Jordan had the look of a predator. The look was due either to the hooked nose which hung from a bald round head, or to the protruding eyes that glittered. The light in his eyes was messianic, though it took Brody some minutes to find out.

"You said my speech to the American Club interested you. I'm glad to hear it. The more people I can reach with my message, the better," he said, shaking Brody's hand and guiding him to the living room area of the office. They sat down. Jordan took a copy of the speech from a pile on the coffee table. "Here, the press only carried extracts."

Brody thanked him and told him why he'd come. "Canada needs leaders, Mister Jordan . . . men like yourself."

"Thank you." The man's smile was expansive. "I try."

"What you said about our competitive enterprise economy . . . " Brody started to say.

"No political party in Canada attaches any importance to it!" interrupted Jordan. "Successful business is tarred in this country as contrary to the interests of the people."

"Right," Brody agreed.

"The existence of any profit is considered socially undesirable," Jordan grumbled.

"Yes," said Brody, "I . . . "

"The noble words 'free enterprise' are interpreted as extortion; the public, victimized by baron monopolies."

"Yes," agreed Brody. But he was suddenly seized by doubt. "What about saving Canada?"

Jordan's eagle eyes seemed glazed. "In an unbelievably obtuse analysis of history today's self-styled 'thinkers' blame competitive enterprise in a free market for the sins of monopoly in a bound market."

"Look . . . " Brody said firmly.

"By an even more spectacular perversion of logic," Jordan ranted, "they advocate that the pendulum should swing to the opposite extreme: from private monopoly to government monopoly."

"Who are you talking about?" Brody interjected.

"Those self-styled 'thinkers' . . . the socialists." Jordan was staring at him. "It doesn't bother them that a government monopoly is just as wastefully inefficient as any other monopoly."

Brody could *see* that point. "About saving Canada, Mister Jordan," he began again.

"We should preach the virtues of the competitive enterprise and the benefits of the free market."

"Yes," Brody patiently started to say, "I thought you . . . "

"Without competition . . . " Jordan abruptly stood up, "we atrophy!" His protuberant eyes were focussed on infinity.

Disgusted, Brody stood up to leave.

"Where are you going?" Jordan asked him in surprise.

"I had hopes you might be interested in saving Canada," Brody said coldly. "All you want to do is complain about socialists."

"*They* are the problem. Here," Jordan vigorously indicated the sofa where they'd been sitting. "Please sit down."

Brody remained standing. "I want to know how you plan to restore Canada. To get people working again. To stop the goddam sell-out!"

Jordan didn't reply. He was uncertain of Brody's purpose.

"Why don't we quit trying to compete with China and Korea in the textile business?" Brody demanded. "Why don't we leave the low cost manufacturing to countries that lack resources; concentrate on what we do best?"

"Because secondary manufacturing means jobs," Jordan answered. "Jobs!"

"We do other things *better*," insisted Brody. "Canada has an educated workforce."

"Jobs!" repeated Jordan stubbornly.

"Products and services!" argued Brody. "High technology products and services. We export them." And when Jordan declined to answer: "We develop and export things like airplanes; air cushion vehicles; rapid transit systems."

"You're wrong," Jordan said firmly. "Canada exports raw materials."

"Okay," Brody agreed, trying one last time. "We should provide food and raw materials to the Pacific Rim countries; they need them. But we should buy back their manufactures too."

"No."

"Yes!" Brody was angry. "They need the foreign exchange so they can buy our airplanes and transit systems."

"No," contradicted Jordan, "our trade is north and south."

"North and south all right," Brody said bitterly. "And it's all between subsidiaries and parents."

Jordan stood up too. "You sound like a socialist," he accused.

"What have you got against socialists?"

"Their beliefs, their purposes, run contrary to the principles of the majority of Canadians."

Brody nodded, unwilling to encourage him any more.

"Their aim is to alienate the consumer from business; to tear

74

down the relationships that have served both business *and* the public so well."

Brody thought of the alienated consumers who lined up each day at the Chinese Embassy.

"They claim businessmen are greedy and uncaring. That corporations are beyond response to consumers' needs. That advertising is false! Prices are padded! Labels are inaccurate!"

Jordan was ranting again. Brody was unimpressed.

"They're striking at the very heart of our free competitive system!"

"What about Canada?"

"Canada?"

"How are we going to save Canada?"

"Oh," said Jordan, surprised.

"I thought you might lead Canada away from union with the States." Brody's tone was accusing.

Jordan examined Brody's stubborn face. "You mean total integration?"

"Yes."

Jordan looked relieved. "You came to the right man. I'm heartily against asking the United States for annexation."

"Would you be a leader?"

The president of the C.M.A. looked at him, uncertain of the proposal, and uncertain of Brody. Finally he nodded. "If my country needs me, I'm ready."

"What do you think Canada should do?" Brody probed.

"Economic integration offers Canada a golden opportunity to fulfill its natural aspirations for both affluence *and* independence."

"What!"

"A free trade area." Jordan leaned over at him. "Don't you see it?"

"For Christ's sake, no!" exploded Brody.

"Canadian manufacturers could escape from the inefficiencies inherent in our tariff protected system."

"Hell," retorted Brody, "our manufacturers would go broke. Production would be centralized down in the States."

"Free trade would lead to equality of incomes between Canadian and American workers."

"What equality is there for the unemployed?"

Jordan switched to a conciliatory tone. "I can see you don't understand."

"That's right." Brody started moving toward the door.

Jordan followed him, talking more rapidly now.

"It's absurd not to realize that this continent is one economic unit . . . and that the U.S. — large as it is — is dependent on Canada; and Canada is dependent on the U.S."

"What about Quebec?"

"You want to keep Quebec in Confederation?"

"Yes, if we can." Brody paused at the door.

"Economic integration would offer French-Canada the opportunity it has long demanded: to compete on equal terms with English-Canada without sacrificing its language and culture."

Brody made mental note to ask Henri about that one. "What about the subsidiaries?" he asked.

"Of American corporations? What about them?"

"Get rid of the tariff and the U.S. corporations will turn their Canadian factories into warehouses."

There was a short, heavy silence.

"There would be a transition period," Jordan said vaguely. "Washington would probably make concessions . . . "

"Imports of manufactured goods would climb," Brody said with finality, "exports of resource materials wouldn't keep up. We go broke either way."

Jordan was stumped. Brody could see it by the way he looked past him. "You are very negative, Mister Brody."

Brody was disgusted. He'd come looking for a leader; all he'd found was a spokesman for the final sell-out. He opened the door. Jordan was at his elbow, apparently anxious for some final word of conciliation, agreement, or polite goodbye.

Brody turned to him. "Did you never realize that in all these years of negotiating with the United States . . . Canada has never won?"

Jordan said nothing. He looked hurt. The injured look added to Brody's irritation.

"Don't you know that we've lost on every treaty, trade pact, water and energy agreement we ever signed with the U.S.? What chance do you think we'd have in a free trade arrangement?"

Again Jordan failed to answer.

"Goodbye," said Brody.

He caught the afternoon bus back to Ottawa.

Professor Burwell seemed disappointed in Brody. He appeared to have expected a disaffected intellectual from the External Affairs Department.

"What brings you to Carleton?" Burwell asked. "My Intellectuals for the Continuance of Canada?"

Burwell was thin, blonde and angry-looking. His office was a cramped and cluttered cubbyhole.

As they sat down Brody asked: "What are your plans for the ICC?"

"Who are you again?"

Brody told him, concluding: "What the country needs is a leader — someone who understands the problems; and who is willing to act."

The professor wasn't enthused. "We're intellectuals. We spend a lot of time trying to understand the problems . . . "

"We need leaders," Brody interrupted.

Burwell shook his head, his thin lips compressed. "Canadians are completely passive. Look at the way they accepted the Civil Unrest Act."

"Canadians *want* independence," Brody assured him, on no evidence whatever.

"The passivity of Canadians as they watched their economy taken over by foreign interests makes me doubt that any of them want to be led to independence."

"They've always believed their leaders," Brody argued. "They didn't realize what was happening."

Burwell looked at him for some seconds. "I don't know," he said at last.

Brody suspected that Burwell was no leader.

"We intellectuals learn more and more about society, but we find the centres of political initiative less and less accessible."

"Are you talking about the centres of communication?" Brody asked. "Communicating with the public?"

"With the *apathetic* public?" Bitterness was in Burwell's voice. "I don't think it makes much difference."

"It's the only public we have," Brody pointed out. "And we still live in a democracy . . . "

"Democracy!" Burwell interrupted rudely, "is merely the way greed and exploitation have been institutionalized."

Brody was startled at the abrupt change. Perhaps Burwell *was* a leader. His hopes rose. "Well what are you going to do?" he asked him.

"What would you *have* me do?" Burwell's anger was now directed at Brody.

Brody reacted with anger of his own. His big fist rested on the desk between them. "To save Canada requires power," Brody said, his hazel eyes boring into the man. "Power means organization. *You* have the beginnings of an organization."

"The ICC?"

"Yes!" Brody's tone was passionate. "Intellectuals could be the nucleii . . . catalysts . . . rallying points for people who want Canada independent." There was a tremor in his voice.

"You don't understand the role the intellectual plays in society."

"You're supposed to *lead* society!"

"That's not true," Burwell said in miffed tones. "The man of knowledge is, after all, legally an employee."

"What?!"

"Subject to everything this fact involves."

"For Christ's sake!" Brody said in disgust.

"Like others in our society, the man of learning is dependent for a livelihood on the job." Burwell hesitated, then added: "The job, of course, being a prime sanction for thought control."

"What is it you're trying to tell me?" Brody demanded.

"To understand is the ideal of the man who has a capacity to know truth but not the chance to communicate it with political effectiveness."

"Canada's hurting! Do you understand why?"

The anger returned to Burwell's eyes and voice. "We live in an industrial civilization," he lectured. "A mass society which imposes a climate of conformity and consensus."

"So god-damn what?" Brody's voice was hard.

"Our large cities lack citizen participation and have no local democracy."

"So?"

"Individual Canadians, Mister Brody, have little to say over how they are governed."

"What *I'm* saying," Brody insisted, "is that the average Canadian would *like* some say."

Burwell leaned back in his chair. The look on his haughty face was one of amused contempt. "You don't understand," he said.

"Of course I don't understand," Brody said. "Tell me."

Burwell was a man of changing temperament. Now he was sincere and earnest. "Due to technology, untold material advancements have been brought to the people of our civilization." He paused.

"Go on," Brody prompted.

"But along with these advancements have arisen forces so menacing they threaten the very foundations on which rest the hopes of those of us committed to the democratic ideal."

"The fascist dictatorships?" Brody asked, feeling better about the man.

"Yes, those . . . but also the police state mentality that is settling on such nominal democracies as our own."

"What's happening to us?"

"With Canada in the throes of breaking up, the ruling elite — the ruling class, if you will — is worried about the continuance of the exploitive monopoly capital system."

"Yes?" Brody said, deeply interested.

"Exploitation and democracy are mutually exclusive. They cannot exist together."

"Why not?" It seemed to Brody capitalism had persisted very well.

"Democracy and exploitation? The one will destroy the other."

It was a difficult point.

"Protest groups?" Brody suggested, thinking of the democratic alternatives.

"Freedom of speech can be a useful safety valve . . . " Burwell's voice became sarcastic, " ... provided that protest never poses a threat to the established order."

"What happens if protest threatens the 'established order'?"

"You should realize that when it feels seriously threatened the ruling class will change the rules."

"What about the Constitution?"

"Canada — the same as any other 'democratic' country in the world today — will use the most violent repressive measures at its disposal ... "

"But why!" Brody interrupted.

" ... if any people's movement threatens the continued existence of the capitalist system."

"What about the socialist movement?" Brody asked, still doubting.

"It has never been a threat. The fact is Canadians are well integrated into the system ... they have no interest in overthrowing it."

"Even with a third of the work force unemployed?"

"Even so. The brainwashing has been complete."

Brody stood up to leave. He was interested in what Burwell had told him, even if the man hadn't turned out to be the leader he was seeking.

They shook hands in the hallway outside. The walls were floor to ceiling in graffiti. "Why do the students do it?" Brody asked.

Burwell didn't seem upset. "It's just a sign of their alienation," he explained. "They resent the system."

"Which one?"

"The university. They know they are here because society has no role for them."

"No jobs?"

Burwell nodded. "We just hold them off the labour market." He chuckled, and added, almost to himself: "Holding pens."

"Pens?"

"The universities across Canada are holding pens. The students know it. So they rebel ... cutting up the furniture, stealing books from the bookstore, destroying those in the library."

"That's rebellion?"

Burwell laughed at his disbelief. "Rebellion — outright revolt — isn't the Canadian way."

80

Richard Hoberman, MP, had come to Brody's attention from afar; that is, from as far as the distance from Brody's seat in the Visitors' Gallery to the floor of the House below. Although Brody spent most of his time there watching the trim figure of the Minister of Research and Development, he also had time to observe the parliamentary hysterics which accompanied the collapsing of Canada.

Hoberman, a former mayor of Edmonton, was scathingly impious in his views of the government's handling of the melancholy situation. Since he was a backbench member of that government, Brody was all the more impressed. Hoberman seemed to Brody the leader Canadians were looking for.

"That's a mistake right there!" Hoberman told him. Two people in the knee-bumping confinement of a junior MP's office in Ottawa is too many. "The last thing Canadians want is a politician to lead them."

"Why?"

"Because federal politicians have had *years* to sort out Canada's problems . . . look at us today."

Hoberman's honest Western manner pleased Brody. He knew that as mayor of Edmonton, Hoberman had been both popular and successful.

"What happened?" Brody asked. "Why didn't the government prevent all this?"

Hoberman sat back in his swivel chair. "You want to know why the federal government can't govern?"

"Yes . . . I'd like your opinions."

Hoberman pulled his desk drawer open to extract a writing pad. "Did you ever wonder what an MP does during all those boring debates in the House?"

"Ah . . . yes," Brody admitted.

Hoberman didn't show Brody the pad he was scanning. He smiled, however, and after a second or two he looked at Brody again. "This MP sits and makes notes to himself on why the government is unable to cope."

"You have a lot of notes there."

"Jesus, yes. But I won't give you the speech . . . I'm not sure whether to do it as a speech, or to go for permanence and make it into a book."

"Summarize it for me," Brody suggested.

"Okay. The reasons the federal government can't govern are these: economic domination by the U.S.; the growth of the international corporations; the dominance of the capital intensive, high technology industries . . . all owned by foreign interests," he added.

Brody nodded, old stuff but true.

"The unemployment problem . . . as technology and capital replaces workers." He flipped the pages of the notes, pausing to scan. "We're non-competitive in world markets . . . due to our high-cost economy."

"It's the Work Ethic," Brody offered.

"Sure. Why not? The rising expectations of everyone in society," Hoberman said, still leafing through his notes.

"Why don't people trust their leaders?"

"One reason," Hoberman sighed, "is the rise of the Myth of the Individual: everyone is as good as anyone else."

It wasn't the answer Brody had expected. "So?" he responded vaguely.

"So people don't look up to their leaders; they don't respect them. People can't be led any more by charismatic leaders."

"Look," Brody's voice grew forceful. "Breadlines . . . at the Chinese Embassy, for god's sake. Unemployeds living in abandoned cars. This country is hurting! We *need* leaders."

Hoberman was unmoved. "People can't be *led* anymore," he repeated.

Brody disagreed, but still held hopes for Hoberman. "What force, or group, can we look to for direction?" Brody asked. "The Civil Service?"

"Jesus!" Hoberman looked anguished; the hand clutching the notes thudded to his desk. "When I think of the hours I spend waiting to kiss the ass of some senior civil servant . . . !"

"Do you *have* to go see them?"

"For my constituents." He grimaced. "I really care about my constituents." Hoberman swung his chair so that he could view the opaque square of light that was the room's only window.

82

"A lot of people — myself more than any, I suppose — criticize the old Civil Service. But when I'm lucid about the problem I admit that it isn't entirely their fault."

"No?"

"The Civil Service is made up of Canadians. People like you and me. They don't want Canada to break up either."

"Then what's wrong with it?"

"Lots of reasons the 'great grey bureaucracy' can't function." Hoberman ruefully touched his notes on the desk. "For one thing, the people in it are demoralized."

"Why?"

"Do you really want to discuss all this?"

"Not if you haven't got time ... but I'm interested in your opinions."

Hoberman smiled, and shook his head. "Flattery ... it's the sure road to this politician's heart."

They laughed at his mock confession, and then Hoberman continued: "The problem exists for everyone who works for the large company, corporation, or government bureaucracy: it's impossible for the individual to relate to the purposes of the organization."

"Alienated," Brody remarked.

"The federal civil servant more than most," Hoberman agreed. "Misdirected by the politicians, confused by the Business Management fads, their merit system scrapped in favour of ability in another language ... " He let the thought fade.

Brody leaned forward in his chair. "How about becoming the leader we need?"

Hoberman shook his head.

"Why not?" Brody was convinced that Hoberman could be the focus of a resurgent Canada.

"The gap between politicians and the Canadian people is horrendous. Secondly: Canadians neither want nor trust leaders."

The warmth of their early conversation was gone.

"I don't think you know *what* Canadians want," Brody said at last.

Hoberman stood up, his face flushed. "Now that Quebec is going, Canadians have seen clearly, and finally, that neither federal politicians nor Ottawa bureaucrats are equipped to solve the problems."

Brody got up to leave. "I think you're wrong," he said. "In times of great need, people do look for leaders. Canada is at one of those times." He began sidling between the file cabinets and the desk to get out.

"Just a second." Hoberman stopped him. "There's one thing I didn't mention."

"What's that?"

"The power structure in this country — there is such a thing you know — does not want a populist movement in Canada."

Brody was irritated; Hoberman had been the most suitable leader he'd discovered. "If the leadership of our country *is* bankrupt," he said with conviction, "don't you think it's *time* the Canadian people started governing themselves?"

Hoberman seemed suddenly older. He looked quite unlike a leader.

"Mister Brody," he said earnestly, "the power structure forbids it."

Chapter 5

September in Ottawa is a kind month; most of the tourists have left, the flowers are still in bloom. Brody enjoyed his evening walk to Parliament Hill. He preferred to follow the path along the canal despite the numbers of people who slept outdoors there.

When the park benches were filled at night, the others lay on the ground. They slept under the bushes, in cardboard boxes, wrapped in coats, tarps, or even newspapers. The wrapped bodies on one grassy embankment reminded Brody of a refugee camp he'd seen just after the war. Yet these were Canadians . . . unemployed Canadians. Brody thought of the situation as he walked.

The police blamed the unemployeds for the wave of street crime; the street violence, in turn, necessitated larger police forces across Canada. Brody, personally, could see little difference between the unemployeds and the hoboes of his 1930s youth. And the hoboes were no crime wave.

By 11 p.m. Brody was the only person left in the Visitors' Gallery to hear the debate about Canada's perishable future. Twenty-seven tired members of Parliament were taking turns listening to each other. Every one of them, it seemed to Brody, was concerned only with the fate of his constituency, province, or region; not with Canada. Of the endless speeches he'd listened to, all had been of the it's-too-late-now, what's-the-best-deal-we-can-make, variety. Such passivity — even if it was in the finest Canadian tradition — disgusted Brody.

With a start he realized that Jan was trying to catch his eye. He waved in reply, glad that she'd decided to call it a night. When she'd disappeared behind the blue velvet curtains he got up from his seat. She was waiting in the hallway below.

"Hi," she said, kissing him lightly on the cheek and then tucking her hand under his arm. "You taking me for coffee?"

"Coffee with the Honourable Minister?" Brody said, as they started down the empty hall. The cold grey stones of Parliament seemed warm and hospitable.

In the foyer were two regular security guards and a Mountie.

"Good night, sir," the guards said to him. The old soldiers seemed to recognize the old soldier in Brody.

"Good night," Brody said. As they passed the expressionless Mountie, Brody said goodnight to him too.

The Mountie did not reply.

Beyond the brass doors they paused at the top of the steps, enjoying the semi-darkness of Parliament Hill which seemed, at that time of night, deserted. Ahead of them, down the second set of steps and along the path, flickered the everlasting flame commemorating Confederation.

"It's my favourite time of day," Jan told him.

"I like dawn," Brody said. But he was ready to exchange dawns for midnights.

"Come on," said Jan. "Let's try my coffee for a change."

As they traversed the empty roadway toward the steps three large figures came out of the shadows toward them. The men wore dark clothing and carried short sticks. Brody peeled Jan off his arm and shoved her back. "Run!" he commanded her.

The first club bounced off his left forearm an instant before Brody's big fist took the man full on the adam's apple. Paralyzed by the shock the man fell, his club clattering to the roadway.

Surprised by Brody's willingness to fight the remaining two attackers hesitated. Then, as Brody turned on them, they began swinging their weighted sticks, the blows raining off Brody's shoulders and arms.

He caught one of the clubs in his left hand, jerking its owner toward him. Brody's right uppercut exploded below the man's eye; a four-inch long, blood-spurting gash blossomed magically. The man dropped, clutching his face.

It was the third man that got Brody. The blow on the side of the head drove Brody to his knees. Before he could rise a boot heel

86

smashed full force against his temple. He didn't feel the rest of the beating administered with boots.

When he regained consciousness it was to find his pounding skull cradled in Jan's lap; she was sitting on the asphalt beside him.

Behind her he could see an ambulance. When the attendants had loaded the two men Brody had felled it drove away. The only person that remained was a Mountie . . . the one who'd been standing in the foyer.

"Get me a cab," Jan said to him. Her voice was shaking with outrage.

She took Brody to the hospital by taxi.

When Brody awoke he lay very still. He guessed what had happened; he'd walked into an airplane propeller. The bruises corresponded to where the blades of the propeller had battered him.

"Oh!" he said, making note not to breathe deeply.

Having mastered breathing faintly he tried the eyes. They were swollen shut and glued with mucous. One of them opened to slit dimension. He discovered his hospital room and remembered Ottawa, Jan, and the fight he'd lost the night before.

"Good morning! How are we feeling this morning?" The nurse walked round the foot of his bed still talking. "Come on, now . . . open that one eye. I saw it open when I came in."

"Good morning," Brody surrendered.

She was a matronly type and Brody liked her better for that. Youth and vigour would have been depressing.

"Hungry?"

"No."

"Thirsty?"

"No."

"Anything?"

"Yes. Where's the bathroom?"

"Oh my no!" exclaimed the motherly nurse tucking the top sheet in tighter. "It's the bedpan for you."

"No!" wailed Brody, and immediately regretted the deep breath it had required.

"Doctor's orders," the nurse said in tut-tut tones. "Concussion."

"What concussion?"

"You may have concussion."

"Oh," Brody said. The thumping in his head made 'concussion' possible. It rhymed with 'percussion'.

"The only time you are allowed out of this bed is to go for your x-rays."

"When do I go for x-rays?"

"Now."

"Good," Brody said firmly. He sat up, nearly fainted, and had to hang onto the nurse while she slid paper slippers on his feet. He sensed her disapproval as she dragged a flannel bathrobe across his shoulders.

"Really!" the nurse said, urging him forward. "A man of your age."

"My-age-what?" Brody winced with the pain of locomotion.

"Fighting."

Brody felt *good* about that. As they proceeded slowly down a long hall he noticed a 'Men' sign on a door. Bedpans be damned.

When he awakened again it was late afternoon. Jan had sent flowers. The card said: 'To Canada's last fighting man'.

Propped on the telephone was a message from Lucille. 'Mr. Robillard will visit you after work'.

"How *are* you, my friend?" Henri asked as he hurried into the room awhile later.

"I'm fine," Brody lied. It still hurt to breathe and he could still only open one eye.

"You *look* terrible."

"Want to know what happened?"

"You were rolled by a gang of unemployeds. I got that from the Mountie doing the investigation."

"Mountie?" Brody queried.

"Federal property; the Mounties are responsible for the Hill area. Don't you think they were 'unemployeds'?"

"I think those clubs were Mountie-issue."

Henri did not appear surprised, but he did look troubled. "Did they look like Mounties?" he said at last.

"It was dark; and they came at me pretty fast. But they were all wearing the same clothes; they had short haircuts; and they all wore boots." Brody twisted his head on the pillow to peer at Henri through his swollen eyelid. "But I hate to think the People's Defenders go round beating the People up."

Henri shrugged. "Times change, Neil. Our police have changed. Incidents like this happen. The question is: why you?"

Brody realized that times *had* changed, that the Territories were a haven, that he'd failed to notice events. "The dead birds?" he asked Henri slowly. "The biological warfare questions?"

Henri hesitated, then: "The police are investigating me also."

"Did they come to your office?"

"No. My friends told me."

Brody was suspicious. "Should your friends be telling you?"

Henri laughed, and patted Brody's bruised shoulder. He didn't notice the wince. "It's one thing a Police State will never control: friendship."

"I hope you're right."

"Human nature," Henri assured him.

"Yes?"

"I have confidence in the English-Canadians."

"I *don't*."

"Just look at how successfully they resisted their government's pressure to learn to speak French."

"Are you receiving guests?"

Pain or no Brody turned his head so his serviceable eye could view Jan in the doorway. She was wearing a beige pantsuit and looked as if she'd just left her desk in the Commons. Emotion cancelled his voice as he beckoned her in.

"Oh, Neil! What have they done to you?" She hurried to the high bed where she examined his battered face. Concern was in her manner as she inspected him. She put her arms round his shoulders and kissed him.

"Don't cry," he mumbled in her ear. The tucked-in sheet prevented him from embracing her. "You didn't cry last night . . . why cry now?"

She pushed away to look at him anew. "Because I was angry last night," she said. "I didn't know you were this badly hurt."

"I'm okay."

"Who were those men, Neil?"

He hesitated. "Henri says the Mounties are doing an investigation."

His non-answer didn't satisfy Jan. "Why did they beat you up?"

"The Mounties told Henri it was a gang of unemployeds."

"What do *you* think?"

"I don't know."

Jan perched herself on the bed beside him. Her proximity awakened his erotic feelings. He wondered, glumly, how sick he'd have to be before Jan's nearness didn't arouse him.

"Neil . . ." she was very businesslike, "could it have to do with the work you're doing for Henri?"

"I don't know," Brody said slowly, "it could have."

"These things happen." She said it as if Brody didn't understand. "We're living in a time of rising violence."

"Yes," Brody agreed. He was willing to let her think him a victim of gratuitous violence.

"Jan . . ." he said suddenly, "I love you."

She looked at him, tears returning to her eyes. "I love you, Neil . . . I always have."

This time he was able to get his arms round her. The embrace was painful, for among Brody's injuries were two fractured ribs.

"I'm hurting you, aren't I?" she said, straightening up.

"A little."

"I'm sorry." She glanced at her watch then stood up to go.

"Don't go."

"I have to."

"So soon?" Brody's pulse lurched as he looked at her standing beside his bed. "When will I see you again?"

"Tomorrow evening."

"How about phoning me?"

"I will." She noticed the flowers. "Did you like my card?"

"I'm not 'Canada's last fighting man'," he protested.

90

"Oh." Mock disappointment tinged her voice. "I thought I really *had* something here." She kissed him lightly and was gone.

"Hey!" he called her back, seeking to prolong her stay. "Is tonight the night?"

"I beg your pardon?" She reappeared in the doorway. "Night for what?"

"The night you give your great speech to the House of Commons and I'm going to miss it because I'm here instead of there?"

"If I *do*," she said, "you'll never get to hear what a great orator I really was."

The evenings the visits of Jan and Henri coincided were memorable. The insights of these two sensitive people never failed to stimulate his need to understand more fully the problems of the country.

Toward the end of his convalescence the desire to do something about the problem made his days difficult. First, however, he had to complete his report for Henri. The report was in the form of pencilled pages in disordered piles.

"Report almost ready?" Henri asked him, gathering a pile of notes from the chair and placing them on the table. Jan, who'd arrived with him, sat on the side of the bed.

"Yes."

"Good. I'll take it with me," said Henri. "Is there anything about it you wanted to tell me?"

"Yes," Brody said. "I want to tell you about Ottawa and this biological warfare thing."

"Was this part of your report?"

"No."

"In that case, tell me . . . and I'll take your report and leave."

"Don't go," Jan said.

"I must." Henri seemed tired, wrung out. He turned to Brody. "Go with your message." It was a phrase from their wartime days.

Brody told him that Canada was not in the least prepared for any kind of an attack involving chemical-biological weapons. "There's a research and development crisis . . . a knowledge gap: our scientists don't even know what's going on."

"Is that right, Jan?" Henri asked her.

She nodded yes.

"There's a paralysis in public health capability. Given a nation-wide epidemic . . . *nothing* could be done by the central government."

Both Henri and Jan were listening closely; there were no arguments with what he was saying.

"Our defence department can provide no defence; there is no civil emergency organization. They even got rid of the Militia," he added as a bitter afterthought.

" 'Inefficient'," Henri said. "That was the reason."

"It figures. The Militia provided the only fighters they had — the farm boys and the street kids who fight *all* their wars — so they disband them."

"What else about this CBW thing, Neil?" Jan brought them back to the subject.

"My last point is departmental rivalries and bureaucratic rigidities. The federal government couldn't respond to an outbreak of aphids."

Henri smiled at them as he stood up to go. "I guess it doesn't matter much anyway."

"How are your talks going with the U.S. ambassador?" Brody asked. "Or are they too secret."

"Very secret, my friends." Henri walked toward the door, the piles of manuscript in his arms. He paused before leaving. "Officially, Washington does not want Canada . . . 'why buy the cow when you can get the milk free'. Is that the concept?"

Brody and Jan smiled at his melancholy joke.

"But," Henri went on, "this is somewhat balanced by the desire of most of the American people to see the United States extend, as one country, to the North Pole."

"Is that leverage?" Brody asked.

"No. We don't negotiate with the American people . . . only their leaders." He waved goodbye. "And the leaders prefer the milk cow idea: more profits."

The next morning, unexpectedly, Henri showed up. He was pale and agitated.

"What's wrong?" Brody said, putting aside the letter he was writing to Lin Lee. He swung his feet over the side of the bed so he could face Henri directly.

Henri sat down. "Toute fini . . . finished."

"What is: your Washington talks?"

"No." Henri lifted a hand to stop his questions. The word 'Washington' apparently reminded him of something else. "Know what an American down there told me the other day?"

"What?"

"The one thing they really admire is the Canadian solution for unemployment: put them behind bars."

Brody was too concerned about his friend to respond to the anecdote. "What's happened? Are you leaving the government?"

"Yes." Henri smiled, but there was pain in his eyes. "A little sooner than I had expected, that's all."

"Why?"

"You."

"The CBW report, or my visit to that 'radical' U.S. professor?"

"Your visit to Professor Ranallo alarmed the Security People. When I tried to defend you, the suspicion fell on me."

They regarded one another.

"The *suspicion* fell on you?" Brody repeated. Then: "Henri . . . I'm sorry."

"Don't be sorry," Henri said calmly. "They've lost two good men, that's all."

"What happened to the birds?" Brody suddenly thought to ask. "Did you ever find out?"

A wry smile lit Henri's face. "Yes," he said, "they were stolen by the CIA . . . sent to U.S. Army laboratories for examination and test . . . and are now being held as evidence that Canada is engaged in clandestine biological warfare research."

"Canada isn't involved in germ warfare research."

"Of course not."

"Then why do they say we are? Do they *believe* it?"

"Their evidence to support the contention is — are you ready — that Canada spends so little on conventional defence, we *must* be relying on biological warfare means."

"And that's the country we're asking to annex us?"

Henri nodded, tears in his eyes. "They despise us . . . did you know?"

"Who?"

"Washington," Henri said. "They despise us for allowing Quebec to leave Confederation."

"Not surprising," Brody said. He didn't understand the emotion Henri was suffering. "They had a civil war over that issue."

Henri looked stricken as he explained: "They're telling Canada and Quebec to get along until the U.S. is ready to integrate the northern half of the continent."

Henri stood up to go. "Your contract has been terminated," he said. "Lucille will have your cheque for you."

He took Brody's hand in both his own. "Goodbye old comrade."

"Are you going to Quebec City?"

"Yes."

"Goodbye, Henri. I'll keep in touch."

"Neil?" Henri was looking earnestly at him. "Go to New Zealand now. Don't wait."

"Have you heard something about me?" Brody asked, alarmed at the urgency in Henri's voice.

"Trust me, Neil. Trust my judgment. Go."

"You think I should leave *now*?"

"Go, Neil."

Long after Henri had gone Brody remained thinking of the reasons for his departure. Is this the way patriots were treated? Could Canada afford to fire such men as Henri?

The country could, of course. He knew that dedicated civil servants such as Henri were expendable; that would-be reformers such as himself were despised. Did it matter?

The man with the food tray came, said hello, left Brody's tray and departed on his rounds. Brody didn't even raise the plate cover to identify lunch. He was too heartsick about Henri.

It was raining when they left the hospital. Forlorn flecks of colour, autumn's first dead leaves, speckled the shiny asphalt as they hurried across the parking lot.

94

"Get in!" Jan said, as they reached her car.

Happy to be together again they embraced, awkwardly, over the gear shift. They looked at each other for long seconds. It was the mutual hypnotic effect they had on one another.

"Have you got the list?" she asked finally, starting the engine, then the wipers.

He handed it to her. "Know where these addresses are?"

She ran her eye down the list. "I think so," she said, then turned to him. "What about Henri's warning?"

"Go to New Zealand now?"

"That's what Henri advised."

"Would you go with me?"

"I could close out my affairs," Jan said evenly. "But what about yours?"

"I have no reason for staying." But his voice sounded vague.

"What about your crusade to save Canada?"

"It's not a 'crusade'," he said, hurt by her choice of words.

"Sorry, Neil." She put the car into reverse. "It's the professional politician in me: I assume that if *we* can't save Canada . . . no one else can either."

"It's okay," Brody said gruffly. "I don't know what can be done, but I'd like to be here in Ottawa, near you."

"Then we stay?"

"Yes."

It seemed like the right decision.

By 4 p.m. they had found what Brody felt answered his needs. It was a huge old living room with towering bay windows. The furniture included a splintery desk and a sagging couch whose broken springs would have attacked were it not for a foam slab.

"Do you drink?" Mrs. Donaghue, the landlady, said to him as the three of them stood in the middle of the room.

"No," Brody said. And since he had been through this many times he added: "And I don't smoke . . . standing, sitting, *or* lying in bed."

Mrs. Donaghue was visibly pleased. She had one more question, and she glanced sidelong at Jan as she asked it: "Will you be entertaining guests late at night?"

"Yes," said Brody, pulling out his month's rent and handing it to her. "But no wild parties."

"There are people living . . . " Mrs. Donaghue pointed at the ceiling.

"We'll be very quiet," Brody assured her.

"Here's the key to your cupboard in the kitchen. Please don't leave any messes for me to clean up."

"I wash my dishes as soon as I'm finished with them," Brody said.

"Good, and will you give me notice when you intend to leave?"

"As much as I can, and at least a week." He walked her to the door.

"You were very charming to your new landlady," Jan said. She had to finish the statement from within the circle of his arms.

He kissed her before answering. "Landladies can make or break a bachelor."

They stood holding one another, not noticing the threadbare carpet, the broken furniture, or the faded drapes. It was a depressing room. But it was what Brody felt he could afford.

"Neil?" she said from against his chest.

"Mmm?"

"What kind of parties?"

"Just you-and-I parties. What did you think?"

She kept her face hidden on his chest. "Do you want me to sleep with you?"

There was a long pause before Brody finally managed to speak. "Yes," he said, "but . . . "

"What?"

"I'd like to ask you to marry me . . . but . . . "

She pushed back to examine his anguished face. "What's wrong?"

"I'm fifteen years older than you."

She was amused at the reason for his distress. Her hand caressed his cheek. "Neil," she said. "I never think about your age."

"I feel young," Brody admitted. "Will you marry me?"

"No."

The look on his face — had she had any doubts about his feelings

— convinced her. She threw her arms around his neck and kissed him. She continued kissing him as he scooped her up and carried her to the relic couch.

"Why won't you marry me?" he persisted.

"When I get out of politics."

"When will that be?"

"I don't know . . . soon."

"Good . . . I'll be happy."

"You mean, you aren't happy now?"

She was teasing him, he knew. "I'll be happier," he tried to explain, "when we can sleep together."

She struggled to sit up.

"What's wrong?" he asked in puzzlement.

"The day when a girl has to marry every damn man she wants to sleep with is over! Where have *you* been?" she demanded.

They collapsed, laughing. And she refused to make love with him.

"Look at those windows!"

"What's wrong with them?"

"People could *watch* us. Those drapes are no help."

He could see her point.

"Come on." She rolled off the couch and began looking for her shoes. "Let's clean this place up."

Afterward Jan took him to her apartment for supper and they spent their first night together.

Surprisingly — for he had dreamt of this night for years — Brody was embarrassed.

"What's wrong?" Jan asked as she raised the sheet and slid in beside him.

When she put her arms around him she discovered what was wrong.

"Scar tissue," he told her. "My back, shoulder and neck."

And at her urging he told her of the wartime crash and the gasoline fire that followed it. "I might have gotten out quicker," Brody concluded, "but I had to make sure everyone else got out first."

"But why?"

"I was captain."

"Oh, Neil!" She kissed him to reassure him.

"Jan," he said gently, "I want you."

"Hi!"

Brody looked up from the editorial pages he had spread on his desk. It was Jan; she came over every noon hour to have lunch with him.

"Come here," he said, beckoning her for a kiss.

On her way she deposited a heavy package on the couch. She kissed him, then asked: "Did you know there's a police car parked outside?"

Brody nodded. "It's been there all morning."

"Are they watching *you*?" She went to the window and looked at the car for several seconds.

"Jan . . . " he interrupted her thoughts, "could someone use me to smear your reputation?"

She came over to his chair, and put an arm across his shoulders. She was looking down at his troubled face. "I expect they could," she admitted. "I thought of it before you were out of the hospital."

"Then why did you . . . ?"

She laid her finger across his lips to stop his question. "Because I don't feel I have anything to be ashamed of." She bent over and kissed him again. "Now, tell me: is that police car keeping track of you?"

"I think so . . . when I came back with my newspapers a guy from the Bell was fixing my phone."

"What was wrong with it?" Jan asked.

"He was putting in a tap."

"Neil . . . they're *spying* on you; why didn't you tell him to take it out?"

"I did." He stood up and put his arms around her. "But he made a good point: leave it in and let them tap . . . and so what? The thing is, I need the phone for radio hotline calls."

Jan searched his face in silence. Then she too set the oppressive feelings aside; there was nothing they could do about their surveillance in any case.

Brody's letters to editors campaign, and now his idea of calling

98

hotline shows, didn't seem practical to Jan. "Aren't you being terribly naive?" she asked.

"Maybe I am," he admitted, "but a lot of people listen to hotline shows."

They stood, arms around one another, happy with the moment. Finally Brody asked her about the package.

"Drapes," she said.

Jan had already covered the foam slab on the couch, bought slip covers for the chairs, a lamp shade and a tablecloth.

"You shouldn't buy drapes," he told her.

She tightened her grip around his neck until, finally, he was obliged to succumb. It was a loving and erotic kiss. Still, Brody was able to chide her: "You shouldn't be buying me anything."

She prodded him playfully. "If I continue coming here to have lunch with you, and we continue doing what we've been doing . . . I want more privacy."

He followed her into the kitchen to tell her about his plans to call hotline programs across Canada.

"You're going to phone long distance?" She handed him a can of soup to open.

"Six-thirty a.m. I can start in Newfoundland; work my way across Canada."

She laughed at his enthusiasm and asked: "Have you figured out what you're going to say if you do get on the air?"

"Sure . . . I'll just tell the people that if they want to save Canada, it will have to be done by themselves . . . because our leaders sure as hell aren't going to do anything."

It took Brody a week to concede defeat. It was past midnight and they were still talking.

"Of all those letters, only one got in," Brody complained. "They printed three sentences out of two pages." Then: "Typed!" he added, recalling the hours he'd spent pecking them out on a rental typewriter.

"How many did you write?"

"Eleven; but each one was different."

Jan hesitated before pointing out what he already knew. "Neil? Don't you agree you're being naive in all this?"

"Maybe," he admitted. "But where does the ordinary person — with no money — start?"

She was silent for a moment, then her arm across his chest tightened in a gesture of comradely compassion. "Your hotline efforts didn't do any better, did they."

"One guy . . . only one guy, in Vancouver, had the decency to call me back collect. I left the same message with all of them."

"But you never got on the air?"

"No. They always ask: 'What do you wish to comment on'? And I say: 'Saving Canada', and that would be all."

"Nothing more?" Jan lifted her tousled head off the pillow to look at him. "That was it?"

"Sometimes they'd put me on hold, but eventually the line would just disconnect."

"You were holding long distance?"

"Yes."

"Oh, Neil . . . you poor baby!"

"One guy called me back," Brody said stubbornly. He stared at water stains on the ceiling, evidences of bygone plumbing disasters upstairs.

"From Vancouver, you said. What did he tell you?"

"He said the radio station paid him a hundred thousand a year to talk about sex with housewives . . . not about saving Canada."

She giggled. "Do they really?"

"Really what?" Brody was not feeling humorous about his failure.

"Do women really call these hotline announcers and discuss their sex lives?"

"I guess so." Brody sighed. "The guy told me if I wanted to discuss orgasms, infidelity, homosexuality, swapping, or just about anything like that . . . he'd be pleased to get me on the air."

"What are you going to do?"

"I still have to gain access to the media; it's the only way I can reach the public."

"Uh-huh." She snuggled closer, her bare torso warm against his own. She sounded sleepy.

"I'm going to Toronto next week to see them."

"Who?"

"A newspaper editor; the publisher, if he's available . . . and the program chief for a TV network."

There was a long silence.

"You asleep?" he finally asked, "or just thinking."

Her hand rubbed his chest. "Neil?"

"Yes."

"You really did miss an opportunity."

"Mmm?" Now he was getting sleepy.

"The housewives of Canada."

"What about them?"

"A grandfather who can make love twice a day, every day? Fascinating."

Chapter 6

The bus ride to Toronto took five hours. Brody sat in air conditioned comfort while outside the tinted glass, sun-blasted rural Ontario unwound. He was too preoccupied with his problem to notice.

Lots of people wanted to save Canada, the problem was to contact them; to get a Movement going. The 'Save Canada Movement'. He thought about the reasons for his Toronto trip.

One: he was going to approach the news media; two, he could contact those political organizations he thought were serious about being 'for' an independent Canada.

The building housing Canada's largest newspaper was impressive. Brody was led by a friendly security guard through the gold broadloomed labyrinth to the office of Al Todd, managing editor. True to the appointment Todd's secretary showed him in.

"Mister Brody, of Ottawa," she said, and closed the door behind him.

"Good trip Mister Brody?" said the genial executive shaking his hand. "Let's sit over here."

The editor, rotund and beaming, looked like a medieval abbot. Brody wondered if the idiot smile was his permanent expression.

"I came to ask why your newspaper isn't doing more to save Canada," Brody said, foregoing idle chitchat.

"Well." Todd leaned ahead, resting fat elbows on fat knees. "We've been editorializing for *years* on the subject of economic domination."

"Articles?" Brody asked.

"Hundreds, no thousands, of inches devoted to the subject." Todd's bald head swung like a metronome. "We at this newspaper care!"

"How come," Brody was surprised at his vehemence, "you didn't print my letter on the subject?"

Todd threw up his hands. "If you could *see* the hundreds of letters we receive each day!" He paused, then leaned forward to confide: "As the largest circulation daily in Canada . . . we are *it* for every crackpot in the country. Not you," he added quickly.

"It's okay," Brody allowed, "but since you *are* the largest paper, don't you have a responsibility to express the concerns of a wider variety of people?"

"We present as many shades of opinion as we can . . . in the limited space we have."

"Two hundred pages is 'limited' space?"

"It's the weight of our advertising burden. We have a heavy responsibility."

"To who?" Brody demanded.

"To all those who depend on newspaper advertising."

"For Christ's sake," Brody complained. "You run page after page of *just* advertising."

"We allot a solid ten per cent of space for news content. Of course, with the cost of newsprint . . . "

"The cost-of-newsprint-what?"

"Mister Liederkranz, the publisher, told me we may have to cut back on editorial again."

"Why don't you run a readers page devoted to the problem?"

"Sometimes we give an entire page to letters. You should read our paper more often."

"I mean a page devoted to letters about the problem of *Canada*. Why don't you devote a page to people like Professor Burwell?"

The editor was shaking his bald head. "A feature like that would require an editor. I can't afford the personnel."

"I'll edit the page for you," Brody offered. "At no salary."

Todd was opposed. "Mister Liederkranz would have to make that kind of a decision."

"Where's *his* office?" Brody asked, standing up to go.

The editor was alarmed at what Brody appeared about to do. His flesh tone had gone from pink to pale. "Have you an appointment with him?"

"His secretary said to stop by."

"Oh," said the pudgy editor, relieved. "Down the hall there." And he added, as Brody opened the door: "I'm sure you'll find he's a most kind and generous man."

"Kind enough to run my letter as an article?"

"It depends on how it's written."

"I have a copy of it here." Brody patted his jacket pocket.

"Leave it with me," Todd invited, the friendliness returning. "I'm sure Mister Liederkranz would send it down to me anyway."

Brody waited outside the office of Christopher Liederkranz. If there was feverish activity associated with bringing out Canada's largest circulation newspaper each day, it was not apparent here. The quiet was almost perfect. It was flawed by the sound of the extraordinarily lovely receptionist cracking her gum.

Just when Brody was about to give up, a man in a blue suit walked past the receptionist, not pausing until he reached the door of the office.

"Oh, Mister Liederkranz!" trilled the girl. "Where *were* you?"

"The men's room, Miss Slater." Liederkranz, following the direction of her glance, looked at Brody. "Are you here to see me?"

Brody nodded, and stood up. "If you have a minute."

Liederkranz had straight hair combed straight back, and the coldest dark eyes Brody had ever seen. "I've got a minute," he said, "come in." As he turned he accepted a yellow message slip from the girl.

Brody followed the publisher into his office. Liederkranz made no gesture toward the living room set but walked directly to his desk. The desk was unusual. It had no drawers and was constructed of clear plastic wrapped around chromed pipes.

Liederkranz sat down leaving Brody to choose from one of two plastic bucket chairs in front. He checked the message slip in his hand. " 'Brody' is it?"

"Yes."

"Girl can't spell." Liederkranz tossed the slip on the desk, making it the only piece of paper visible in the office. "What did you wish to see me about?"

104

Brody felt uncomfortable. "I came to ask why your newspaper doesn't print more on the Constitutional Crisis."

"What!?" Liederkranz was immediately angry. "We print more about *that* than any other newspaper in Canada . . . including Montreal papers, French *or* English."

"No," Brody found himself soothing the man, "I mean 'different' views; other people's."

Liederkranz looked at him, obviously regretting his compulsive generosity in inviting him in. "Whose views? Yours?"

"Well, mine for one."

"And what are *your* views?" The tone was icy.

"I think the people of Canada should be allowed the chance to solve their own problems."

"We have something called 'Parliament', Mister Brody. It's all set up."

"No, no," Brody hurried to explain. "Parliament — the federal government — isn't equipped to solve the problems."

"What do you suggest? Dissolving Parliament?"

"That's probably going to happen anyway," Brody said. "But I'd advocate scrapping the form."

"In favour of what, Mister Brody."

The repeated use of his name was sarcasm, but Brody ignored it. "I don't know exactly what, but the people of Canada need a new form of government. One more responsive to the needs."

"What 'needs'?"

"The problems: poverty; unemployment; regional disparities. Our parliamentary form of government is unsuited to solving these problems."

"Have you any idea," Liederkranz' voice was laden with sarcasm, "of what it is you're complaining about?"

"Yes. Parliament is made up of the professional classes — primarily lawyers — and the well-to-do." Brody's temper rose. "None of them have a goddamn clue what's hurting the people."

"And what do you suggest, Mister Brody, as a replacement?"

"I don't know."

"You 'don't know'?"

"I'd let the people decide for themselves."

"But you have no suggestions to 'guide' us in our quest for a better mode of government?"

Stung by the sarcasm Brody paused, then offered: "Instead of two political parties and three hundred members of Parliament, how about fifty Board members nominated by the groups who know them: their unions and trade associations."

Liederkranz sat mute. So Brody added: "A Board of Directors replacing Parliament."

And when the publisher failed to respond again Brody advanced his other ideas. "How about starting an 'Open Forum' page? A letters page. Maybe full page articles by thinkers such as Professor Burwell."

"Articles by 'thinkers' such as yourself?" murmured Liederkranz.

"Sure!" Brody affirmed. "I'll even edit the page."

"Spare me the pleasure of your presence on my staff," Liederkranz mocked.

"I'll do it free."

"Spare me."

"You could run a series on the State of the Revolution."

"Revolution?" The publisher's dark eyebrows shot up. "It sounds to me as if you don't know *what* you're advocating."

"I'm advocating the return of the powers of governing to the people."

They glared at one another over the gleaming plastic. Brody realized the publisher's arrogance was based on a lifetime of bullying; and that this prerogative rested on the man's inherited wealth.

"Have you ever thought of emigrating to China, Mister Brody? You might like it there."

"The Chinese people are great," Brody said. His big fist was laid emphatically on the desk top. "We have a great deal to learn from them. But this is Canada . . . here, and now."

"There are many socialist organizations already working for what you seem to espouse, Brody. May I suggest you contact them?"

"Who have you got in mind?"

"There's the Maoists . . . I think they're calling themselves 'Socialists for Canada' this year . . . " he waited for Brody to jot it down.

"Then there's what remains of the old Waffle . . . the 'Movement for an Independent Socialist Canada'."

Brody wrote that name and then looked up at Liederkranz. "Any more?"

"You could talk to the vestigial remnant of the NDP." And as Brody was noting that, Liederkranz added: "All of these groups have offices in Toronto."

"Do you give these groups space to outline their programs?" Brody asked.

"Good God, no! Why would I do that?"

"The public's right to know."

Liederkranz looked surprised. He'd given a speech with that same title the week before to the Publishers Association. But now he said: "The 'Freedom of the Press' implies my freedom *not* to print subversive doctrines."

Brody coolly regarded the hard-eyed man. "Freedom of the Press, you're telling me, belongs to the man who owns one?"

The publisher looked at him for a long moment. "That's true, Mister Brody. And you can buy *my* newspaper. I'll sell it to you for a trifling one hundred and fifty million."

Brody stood up. "I'd want your TV stations, weekly newspaper chain, and the syndicated news services too. And you wouldn't be including those for a hundred-and-a-half."

Liederkranz smiled, wolfishly. "Of course not," he said.

"Is that Mister Brody? Come right over; Mister Newton is expecting you."

As it turned out, Morton P. Newton, executive vice-president, programming, had mistaken the name 'Brody' for a broadcast licensing official of the same name.

"Since you came all the way out here," Newton said, "come in."

Newton was dumpy, rumpled, and late middle-aged. Overwork — a lifetime of it — had worn permanent scars on his face.

"Push them on the floor," he told Brody, indicating a pile of manuscripts on the guest chair.

Brody found parking space for them amid the piles on the man's desk. "I'm sorry it's so late in the day," he apologized, "but I didn't arrive until noon hour."

Newton smiled a tired smile. "I never get away before seven; what is it you came for?"

"I'm trying to interest the media in broadening their coverage of the Constitutional Crisis."

The TV executive closed his eyes, groaning: "We're doing it to death!" He opened his sad eyes. "People just aren't interested, our news announcers are begging me to do just one newscast without mentioning it."

"Surely . . . " Brody started to object.

"It's boring."

"But surely it's the biggest news story we've ever had . . . our country breaking up."

Newton nodded. "That's why I insist on carrying something on it every newscast. But it's boring; I admit it. All those talking heads."

"But it's news isn't it? Important news."

"It may be." The executive sighed. "But it's not television. It's not entertaining."

"The 'news' is entertainment?"

"Of course. People expect to be entertained . . . by the news just as much as by any other TV show."

"Riots, wars, crime?" Brody was incensed. "Most of the important news is just talking."

"That's right . . . but in complex situations — such as the one we have with Canada today — people can't understand what it's all about."

"Is that why TV news is *always* superficial?"

Morton P. Newton was patient. "Most news is superficial."

"Something's wrong!" Brody exclaimed. "We drift into these situations — Quebec, for instance — as a result of being told the wrong things . . . or from having had things presented to us in a simplistic way."

Newton explained it once again. "People don't get their news that way because *we* give it to them; nor because *we* are bad. They get it that way because they want it that way: simplistic."

108

Brody tried a different approach. "All those interviews you do on Parliament Hill."

"Yes?"

"Why are they always with MPs? Government leaders, or opposition leaders. Why don't you interview *non*-government people?"

"We do. Academics, economists, Constitutional buffs."

"No," Brody hurried to explain, "socialists, radicals, people with differing views. Not the same old parliamentary nit pickers."

Newton smiled his weary smile. "You've asked me two questions: parliamentary nit pickers, or people with differing views. Which are you the most interested in?"

"Look," Brody urged the phlegmatic executive. "Why don't you use a guy like, say, Professor Burwell? He's knowledgeable, and he lives in Ottawa. Let *him* interview our government leaders. He knows the questions that need asking."

Newton shook his head. "Burwell's a radical; Public Affairs is objective."

"How about Richard Hoberman, the MP? He'd ask tough questions."

"I should give him a platform?"

Brody could see the man's point. Still, he lodged a complaint. "People are tired of watching these friendly chitchat sessions where the interviewer never asks an embarrassing question. As if they were all rehearsed in advance."

"They probably were," Newton admitted. "But you have to realize that the interviewer works there in Ottawa; he's dependent on these guys as news sources . . . he has to keep their goodwill."

"That's 'managing the news' !"

"I suppose it is. But it's not *our* fault; we can't control the news source. If the Minister of External Affairs tells us lies every day of the week, we can only carry his lies to the people."

"Surely you could carry an editorial statement."

"We're in a high visibility business. Politicians watch themselves on TV, plus any other programs that affect them." The tired smile returned. "Mister Brody, no benefits accrue to broadcasters from carrying controversy."

"But couldn't you interview people like myself, who have different views from those of the government?"

"How different?" Newton was looking at him with world weary eyes.

"I think Canadians could solve the problems facing Canada if only they were given the chance to do so."

"How would you suggest they start?"

"By scrapping Parliament, first."

Newton held up a hand to stop him. "That's enough." He put his hand back down. "Do you want me to tell you?"

"Tell me what?"

"About the government and the industry."

"Yes, please do." Brody was grateful for his candour.

"The government will guarantee the economic interests of the broadcasting industry . . . as long as the media give the government favourable coverage in return."

Brody was shocked. "Is that true for both the major parties?" he asked.

"They're interchangeable; no difference."

"So interviewing critics of the government is not in your interests?"

"Mister Brody," said the sad-eyed man, "I wouldn't *sell* time to a radical."

"There's no way for people with different views to gain access to the media?"

Newton smiled at him. "What people like you don't realize is that access to audience must be earned with talent." He waited for a moment, then added: "People watch TV for entertainment; if it doesn't entertain, they won't watch."

Brody knew that was true. When he didn't respond, Newton finished: "Would you recognize the right of the viewer to trivia?"

"I guess so," Brody said, discouraged. "Any suggestions on how I can reach the Canadian people?"

"You can buy space in the newspapers. They aren't like us, you know . . . dependent on government licensing."

When Brody arrived at the address of the Maoist 'Socialists for Canada Movement', he found it to be the basement of a dingy restaurant. Rudy and Lionel, the teenagers waiting amid stacks of dusty political tracts, were not what he envisioned when he thought of Youth-to-save Canada. They called each other 'Comrade Rudy' and 'Comrade Lionel'. They had short hair and wore identical army style khaki jackets. Neither of them looked robust. 'Red Rudy', as he told Brody he was interchangeably known, was fat; Comrade Lionel was reed thin. What they had in common was an aura of hysteria.

"I take it your Socialists for Canada Movement is based on socialism," Brody said politely as they sat down at a wobbly wooden table.

"To pursue independence seriously," Red Rudy intoned, "is to make visible the necessity of socialism in Canada."

Brody glanced at Lionel who was staring at Rudy. The laundry tubs, the concrete walls, the exposed plumbing and low-wattage light bulbs, gave the Socialists for Canada Movement an inane subversive cast.

"Will I get the tap?" whispered Lionel.

Rudy nodded. He waited until Lionel had turned on the tap over the laundry tub before explaining it to Brody. "The Mounties," he said over the rushing water sounds. "They have us wired."

Brody glanced round the basement with mild interest. "Where?"

"Everywhere." Rudy paused for effect. "Our phones are tapped; the office is bugged; our *parents'* phones are tapped."

When Brody didn't reply, Rudy added: "They trail us everywhere we go."

"Oh?" Brody found it hard to believe.

"Taking pictures."

"Who?" Brody asked.

"The Mounties." And when Brody remained skeptical he added: "You'll see. When you walk out that door you're going to get your picture taken."

"By who?"

"Who's on duty, Comrade Lionel?"

"The little one with the sunglasses."

Brody couldn't take them seriously. Since he wanted to visit the other activist organization — the Movement for an Independent Socialist Canada — he thought he'd hurry this one along. "What is your goal?" he asked Rudy.

"The Socialists for Canada Movement arises out of the working class and is the organized political detachment of that class," recited Rudy.

"Are you affiliated with any labour groups?" Brody asked.

Without altering his expression Rudy monotoned: "The outlook of our movement is a world outlook, that of Marxism-Leninism, which embodies the struggles of the working people . . . the theory and practice of socialism."

"Are you . . . ?" Brody started to ask.

"The science of socialism does not arise spontaneously out of the labour movement." Rudy's shifty eyes flitted past Brody's.

Brody glanced at Lionel who was staring, slack-jawed, at his leader. Brody turned to Rudy too. "But you're not, actually, supported by a union," he said.

"Our movement — through its work, its teachings, its leadership of struggles — fuses scientific socialism with the labour movement . . . and by doing so it spreads political consciousness among the workers." Rudy's voice began to rise; perhaps loud enough to be recorded over the rushing water sounds. "We're providing the workers an awareness of their historic mission as a class!"

"Look," Brody said firmly. "I'm going over to the Movement for an Independent Socialist Canada."

"Those social fascists," sneered Lionel.

"What the hell is a 'social fascist'?" Brody asked.

"Establishment socialists," Rudy exclaimed, losing his disciplined cadre leader look. Both boys seemed anxious to keep him there with them. "Instead of struggling over political lines, they resort to red-baiting and intimidation of SFCM and other militants."

"Is S.F.C. . . . . you?" Brody interjected.

Rudy nodded. "Their sole object is to abort any challenge to the nationalist politics and the equivocation of their own leaders."

Brody hadn't the faintest idea of what Rudy was talking about. He stood up to go. The two boys leapt to their feet.

"There's more," Lionel said, "there's lots more." And when he had Brody's attention he added: "We've got guns hidden away; and guerrilla training camps in the Gatineaus."

Brody was, in spite of himself, surprised. "How many of you are there?" he asked. He'd had the distinct feeling there were but two in the entire Movement.

"Lots," Rudy said, "we can't tell you how many because we're in cells."

"Oh?" Brody was doubtful, and he started toward the door.

The two boys were right beside him.

"We change our names," Lionel said. "I'm using three myself right now."

"We've got plans for the new currency," revealed Rudy as Brody opened the door. "And designs for stamps."

Brody climbed the stairs, the two boys at his heels. "Currency and stamps for the new independent Canada?" he asked them. He was convinced they were babes in the woods.

"For *after* the revolution," Rudy said happily.

Bright daylight made Brody squint as they emerged on the sidewalk beside the restaurant. A little man, with strands of black hair draped carefully across a tanned bald head, but whose eyes were protected by aviation style sunglasses, left the mailbox he'd been leaning on and came toward them. He stopped, then opened his jacket to reveal a camera which he raised to his eye, focussing on Brody and the two revolutionaries. He clicked the shutter.

"Want another?" taunted Rudy as the man sidled back to the mailbox.

There was no reply.

"You see?" Lionel said. "Didn't we tell you?"

Brody nodded. "Goodbye, boys. I guess I'll go visit the social fascists."

"Beware," Rudy dead-panned, "the old harlot of social democracy."

Again Brody didn't know what the hell Rudy was talking about.

The sign in the window said 'Movement for an Independent Socialist Canada'. A bell suspended above the door tinkled as he came in. It had once been a barber shop; wooden folding tables and cracked plastic chairs had replaced the barber thrones. A pleasant looking woman sat at one table.

"Is this the Waffle?" Brody asked.

The young woman had an air of forthright confidence. "Yes," she said, "what can I do for you?"

"What's being done to save Canada?"

"From breaking up? Or from joining the U.S."

"Both."

The woman smiled, stretching her hand across the table to shake his own. "I'm Bernice Thorpe," she said, "executive-secretary. Who are you?"

Brody told her, and as they sat down on opposite sides of the table he concluded: "What's being done, now? Who is prepared to lead? Who is following? What specific program has anyone underway to save Canada?"

Bernice studied him. Brody realized that she thought him an eccentric.

"Nobody's leading, Mister Brody. Nobody's prepared to follow. There are no programs for saving Canada."

"What about your organization?"

She sighed. He had touched on a painful subject. She quit looking out the front window and looked directly at him again. "You want to know why the Canadian Left is unable to provide any leadership?"

"Yes," said Brody. "That's what I'm trying to find out."

"There are lots of reasons: I don't want to clutter up your mind so I'll give you the big ones."

"Go ahead," invited Brody, "clutter up my mind."

She was amused, but the smile departed as she explained: "The Left has always been torn by forces within itself." She hesitated.

"What else?" prompted Brody.

"North America has a capitalist economy. The people are brainwashed. No matter what tragedies unfold people will continue to support it."

"And people think 'socialist' is a dirty word?"

"Very dirty."

Brody wondered how long she had been sitting there; how many people came in to use the reading tables. Why did she do it if the socialist cause was so hopeless?

"What's required?" Brody asked her.

"If Canada wants independence, it will have to go socialist."

"Why?"

"Anything less will fail. Capitalism is, after all, stronger than any government."

"The U.S. government?"

"The U.S. government included."

Brody found the office of the New Democratic party above a row of boarded up stores. The proprietor, Patrick Symington, a poor student grown to poor adult, was waiting for him.

"Come in, Mister Brody," he said, gesturing a welcome. "It's small, but it's the only riding office in Toronto."

"What about the Movement for an Independent Socialist Canada?" Brody asked. "I was just over there."

"That Waffle drop-in centre!" Symington cantilevered his six-foot-three body into a chair. "They're a sect, not a political party."

"I'm looking for leaders," Brody explained, "people who are prepared to save Canada."

The riding secretary removed his glasses and began polishing them.

Brody continued: "An editor . . . Al Todd, I think his name was, suggested I see you."

"Oh yes; I write Todd letters to the editor." Symington sat blinking, apparently ready to let the conversation lapse.

"What does your party propose Canada do?"

Symington seemed grateful for the question. "We believe in the two nation concept of Confederation; we call it 'co-operative federalism'."

"But it's all gone!"

"Because Quebec is opting out?"

"For Christ's sake, that 'two nations' crap just greased the skids for their departure."

Symington was deflated but he rallied: "Our party believes in equal partnership, French and English. When Quebec is gone, we hope they will consider sharing things with what remains of Canada."

"Such as?"

"The federal budget; foreign trade; tariff policies."

Brody was astounded. "What about this movement to ask the U.S. to annex us? Where does your party stand on *that*?"

"We don't make policy on rumours," Symington remarked primly.

"Okay," Brody agreed, irritated with the non-answer. "You call yourself a socialist party . . . "

" 'Social democrat', there's a big difference."

"Okay, but people are apt to link socialist principles with your name. Right?"

"Yes," admitted Symington, blinking rapidly.

"Would the NDP nationalize U.S. subsidiaries?"

Symington shook his head. "That," he said, "is self-defeating. You nationalize the factory and are left with the empty shell: devoid of the American know-how that made it successful in the first place."

Brody didn't agree about the magical know-how but he sensed that Symington had argued the point many times. "What *does* the NDP believe in?"

Symington cleared his throat, happy to have been asked. "Although we have no sitting members in the House of Commons, we still see ourselves as being able to exert a socialist influence." He looked at Brody expectantly.

"A pressure group?" Brody responded.

"Yes, if you will." Symington relaxed, slumping to Brody's eye level. "Since capitalism is not about to be displaced as the dominant economic system, we hew to a bore from within policy."

Brody — imagining busy socialist politicians 'hewing and boring' in the House of Commons — didn't answer.

"We pursue a theme of enlightened welfare," Symington concluded.

"With who?"

"With both the major federal parties."

It bothered Brody. He recalled Morton P. Newton's remark about the old line parties: 'they're interchangeable; no difference'.

"You call yourself a social democrat: you haven't mentioned the

116

class conflicts that exist in this country." Brody was tired of the pointless discussion.

Symington pointed a long index finger at him. "You think there's a big division line between the mass of the people and the wealthy few, don't you?"

"Yes," admitted Brody. "Something like that."

"Well it's not true. The split is between the majority of Canadians who have jobs . . . who enjoy some measure of affluence at least . . . and the minority who do not."

"Nearly half the working population is out of work," Brody reminded him. "It's a depression. Where's the 'affluence'?"

"You don't understand. These people — even the unemployeds — don't see it as a depression. They see *themselves* as failures; not the system failing them."

"Surely you socialists could organize them; the blue collar workers and the unemployeds."

Symington shook his head in flat denial. "It's not true. The blue collar workers are affluent. They see welfare programs as money taken from their own pockets."

Brody knew it was true. No one really wants to help his neighbour.

"The struggle," Symington concluded, "is against the poor."

When Brody arrived back in Ottawa it was to find his room transformed. All that remained of the original furnishings was the battered desk.

"How much did it cost you?" he asked Jan.

"That's my secret. What I want to know is: do you like it?"

"Of course," said Brody, standing with his arm round her waist. They were looking at new wallpaper and freshly painted woodwork.

"Do you *really* like it?"

"It doesn't look like the same place."

"Good! I want you to have a nice place to work."

For the next two days Brody laboured over a document which summed up his feelings and opinions about the present plight of Canada.

"It's a one shot," he told Jan when he showed it to her. "A full

117

page in four dailies: Vancouver, Edmonton, Winnipeg and Toronto."

"Aren't you forgetting the Maritimes?"

"Well, I don't figure the Maritimes and Newfoundland will want to bother with the rest of us."

"Why don't you let *them* decide that?"

"Okay. What do you think of it?" he asked her.

"Pretty strong stuff. Do you think it will make any difference?" She paused, then: "Other than wiping you out financially?"

"I don't know," Brody said. He reached for her hand and pulled her down beside him. "What do you think?"

"Sitting in the Commons listening to it day after day . . . " She turned toward him. "Neil, I swear my mind is turning to mush." Her mouth fell open, her eyes rolled upward . . . crossed and, finally uncrossed.

Her caricature impression of a porridge-brained parliamentarian was so funny that Brody broke up.

"But do you think it will do any *good*?" he asked her.

"I doubt that it will affect the Canadian people in any way," she said truthfully.

SIX QUESTIONS FOR CANADIANS

Q: Where is Canada today?

A: Economic depression (poverty; unemployment; inflation); squandered resources; urban *and* rural blight.

Q: How did we get here?

A: Through the greed of the Canadian ruling class, the people who sold our forests, our minerals, our land, for the short-term gain; aided, down the decades, by power-hungry Canadian politicians.

Q: Why is Quebec leaving us?

A: Because she cannot trust English-speaking Canada to protect her interests in the world. Quebec no

118

longer wants to be part of the great Canadian sell-out.

Q: What *are* Canadians?

A: Canadians are:
  a) racists — ask our native peoples;
  b) war criminals — we've profited shamelessly from American imperial wars since the 1960s;
  c) dupes — we've believed there is such a thing as a 'free' lunch.
  But: Canadians can also be courageous, loyal, hard-working.

Q: So what is wrong?

A: We've allowed our morally bankrupt political leaders to substitute social welfare band-aids for genuine economic reform. Not only are these political leaders morally bankrupt, they are incapable of suggesting ways by which Canada might survive as a national entity.

Q: What *has* to be done?

A: The answers to Canada's problems don't lie with party-hack politicians ... they lie with the people. The Canadian people must assume power for their own direction and destiny.
  The answer to every problem lies with the people!

The full page ad that Brody placed in the major daily newspapers in Canada attracted little attention.

Chapter 7

Anxious for reaction to his ad, Brody walked each morning to a news-stand. As he strode through the streets he had time to note the signs of economic depression. Buildings were abandoned part way through construction. Grass grew out of cracked concrete beams, reinforcing steel hung like brown entrails and rust from the rods stained the walls like patches of dried blood. City pavements were cracked, potholes unfilled, uncollected garbage bags lined the curbs. A meat market had a sign: 'No meat'.

Reaction to his ad came in the form of a young man at his door. "Mister Brody? I'm from Canadian Press; I'd like to interview you."

"About what?"

"It's about the ad you ran: 'Six questions for Canadians'?"

"Oh," said Brody, pleased. "Come in." And as they crossed the room he asked: "How did you find me?"

"It was easy," the young reporter said. "I just called the Mounties. I figured anyone like you would be known to the cops. You were!" he chuckled as he sat down and flipped open his note pad. "I understand you were a war hero. Do you want to tell me about it?"

"The War has nothing to do with the plight of Canada today."

The reporter looked earnest and concerned. "I understand you're a failed businessman; do you wish to discuss that?"

"For Christ's sake . . ." Brody marvelled at the question. "I sold my half of a partnership. Why would I want to discuss that?"

"Surely your own failure in the economic system has embittered you. Isn't that the real reason you composed and ran the ad?"

"No," Brody protested. "That had nothing to do with it."

As Brody tried to keep the topic on Canada's troubles — and all that wasn't being done to alleviate the problems — the reporter persisted in discussing Brody's mental welfare.

"You've never remarried, Mister Brody. Surely this denotes a degree of unhappiness. Wouldn't you say?" And while Brody stifled a rude answer, the reporter scribbled furiously in his notes.

"I understand," the young man continued as he finished scribbling, "that you were fired from your government job. Do you wish to tell me about that?"

"I wasn't *fired* from any job," Brody said, "I was on contract; I completed the work I was contracted to do."

"My information is that you never completed it. That you were, in effect, fired."

Brody wondered what the interview was supposed to be about. "Mister . . . I didn't catch your name?"

"Scholl. Herbert Scholl."

"Mister Scholl. The problem that concerns me is Canada. *What* are we going to do about Canada?"

The reporter turned over a page; a fresh start. Brightly he looked at Brody. "What is your connection with the radical groups?"

"*What* radical groups?"

"Your name has been associated with those of radicals."

"Such as?"

"Professor Ranallo, for one. 'Red Rudy' Redke, for another."

Brody controlled his welling anger. "Where do you get this kind of information?" he asked.

"It's all part of the backgrounding we do before writing a story. CP wire copy, you know, goes to every daily in Canada. We have to be accurate."

"Look, Mister Scholl. If you aren't here to discuss Canada's problems; if you're not interested in *my* concerns for these problems . . . we might as well stop right now."

The young man looked troubled. He glanced down at his notes, then again at Brody. His eyes shifted from Brody's and travelled round the room. Finally he said: "You . . . are the story. My editor told me not to get involved in political discussion."

"But *why?*"

"Well," the reporter was uncomfortable, "for one thing, the Confederation Crisis is being flogged to death. Practically everything coming out of the Press Gallery concerns it."

"So?"

"So the story my editor wants is a personality story."

"To hell with your editor!" Brody roared, standing up and glaring at him. "I'm interested in saving Canada!"

"But that's a non-story," Scholl said, sadness in his voice. He got up to go.

"It's the only story you're going to get around here," Brody said firmly as he escorted him to the door.

Brody was wrong, of course.

Man who wants to save Canada

OTTAWA (CP) — An elderly eccentric in a lonely rented room wants to save Canada.

At a time when the nation's constitutional future appears in doubt, many Canadians may share the sentiment.

Few would do what Neil Brody did: take out a full page ad to express his feelings to Canada at large.

The ad, which appeared in five leading Canadian dailies earlier this week, called on Canadians to "assume power for their own direction and destiny."

Who is this would-be prophet?

He is a former war hero, a much-decorated bomber pilot of World War II. After the war, he returned to the North where he started a bush-flying business.

"He was never much of a businessman, from what I gather," said Pete Brillo, hard-driving, Los Angeles-based president of Air Bear, the company that took over most of the contracts that once went to Brody and Lee Aviation.

Brody left Hay River after all those years flying in the North and came to Ottawa. A friend — no longer employed by the government — offered him a contract for services; a report.

"We never saw his report," said a spokesman for External Affairs who declined to be named. "We aren't even sure what the report was about."

The spokesman said Mr. Brody's contract had been terminated before the ad appeared.

A failure in business, a failure as a government contractor, old-soldier Brody sought the solace of radicals.

In rapid succession he was associated with the Maoist-backed Socialists for Canada Movement; the Movement for an Independent Socialist Canada; and the New Democratic Party.

According to National Security headquarters in Ottawa, Brody tried all the dissident groups in Canada without, apparently, finding a political home in any of them.

What strange compulsions drive a man like this?

Said Dr. R. B. Arbuthnaught, director, Social and Life Sciences, University of Toronto: "Psychically damaged during the war, life damaged afterward, he contemplates a world he did not make and which he cannot understand."

The man at the door was in civilian clothing but Brody recognized him for what he was; he and his partner.

"Mister Brody?"

"Yes."

"I'm Sergeant Godfrey..." he opened an identity card folder and showed Brody a card with his photograph and the word 'Police' overprinted.

Brody glanced at the second Mountie who stood a few feet down the walk. At the curb was a patrol car.

"Yes, Sergeant?"

"I'll need your passport, sir."

Brody was surprised.

Godfrey was tall, powerfully built, and reminded Brody of men he'd known in the war. That is, he was the type of man Brody would normally respect.

On impulse, and out of curiosity too, Brody said: "I'm about to make a cup of tea, Sergeant... care to join me?"

Godfrey hesitated, studying Brody's face for a moment before turning to the other man. "Wait for me in the car."

In the kitchen, while Brody was baptizing the tea bag, Godfrey told him his passport had been revoked, "... under the permit to travel section of the Civil Unrest Act."

Brody led the way back to the living room where they sat down. He asked Godfrey what other types of permits were required under the Act.

"Just the basic things," Godfrey said easily. "Permits for publications, picket lines and assembly."

The word caught Brody's attention. "What kind of 'assembly'?" he asked.

"Assemblies of more than ten persons."

'Ten persons' would even rule out lawn bowling, Brody thought. "Do you enforce *all* these regulations?"

Godfrey smiled at Brody's quizzical inflection. "No... the government passed it as just-in-case legislation."

The Mountie had an honest look that Brody liked. He wondered whether Godfrey ever asked himself about the civil rights aspects of such laws.

"Just-in-case what?" Brody probed.

Godfrey told him that the times required such legislation to permit the government to protect itself.

"From what?"

Godfrey refused to be pinned down. Instead, he finished his tea and said: "Surely you'd grant the government the right to protect itself."

" 'Protect itself' from *what*, Sergeant?" And when Godfrey refrained from answering, Brody added: "Are you talking about the 'government' . . . or the power structure behind the government?"

Godfrey handed back the mug. "I'll need your passport, Mister Brody."

Brody got him the document. As he escorted the Mountie to the door he said: "Is it your argument that Democracy must be allowed to defend our freedoms . . . against our own people?"

Godfrey slid Brody's passport into the inner pocket of his jacket. There was regret in his voice as he said: "Someone has to defend your freedom."

As he watched the patrol car pull away he recalled Henri urging him to leave at once. Too late now; the government wouldn't let him go. He wondered who protects people from the 'defenders' of democracy.

Brody did not tell Jan that he intended to interview — if possible — one of her Cabinet colleagues. He didn't tell her because he couldn't define a purpose for the visit other than that the Minister of Health and Welfare held the drawstring. That is, he controlled the trickle of dollars which allowed the starving people of Canada to starve more slowly.

With his briefcase Brody looked as ordinary as any civil servant visiting the Hill on business. To the security guard at the side entrance to the Parliament Building he announced cheerfully: "Dan Springate."

"Do you know where Mister Springate's office is, sir?" the guard asked him.

"I was there once," Brody lied, "but I forget the number."

124

"Three-oh-nine, sir. Top of the stairs, to your right; about half way down the hall."

When he opened the door it was to find the receptionist reading a novel.

"Are you here to see the Minister?" she asked him.

"Yes," Brody said. "I am."

"You'll have to wait." She indicated a visitor's chair. "The Minister is dictating; he'll be with you in a minute."

The ante-room Brody and the girl shared was small. The furniture was modern, the broadloom cushioned, the walls were panelled in rich dark wood. The narrow Gothic window was inadequate to its function.

The receptionist stood up, purse in hand. "I'm going to the cafeteria. Would you care for a coffee?"

"No thanks," said Brody.

Brody was alone in the ante-room when the Minister opened his office door and beckoned him in.

"Let's get this over with," Springate directed as he settled onto his sofa and pointed his cigar at the chair opposite. "Sit down."

Brody was amazed at his own luck. Springate had mistaken him for someone else. He sat down, looking at beetle-browed Dan Springate, one of the Cabinet Inner Five.

The Minister was fat and dynamic. He had amassed millions manipulating government contracts to develop undeveloped areas of Canada. These areas, despite his talented efforts, had stubbornly stayed undeveloped long after he'd left for Ottawa.

"What do you want to hear?" Springate rumbled, circumcising the cigar with one deft bite. Thwob! It bounced off the side of his desk.

"With all the problems facing our country today," Brody said, watching ignition, "I was wondering about the problems of a busy Cabinet minister such as yourself."

Springate took a long appreciative pull on his cigar. Behind the blue haze his features were in repose. He liked Brody's question. "Pressures," he said. "No one could imagine the pressures."

"Can you tell me about them?"

"Well, you've got pressures from the riding."

"Your constituents?"

"No." Springate didn't bother to explain. "And you've got Party pressures." He waved the cigar, stirring the haze around him. "And you've got the Civil Service."

"Inefficient?" Brody murmured.

"They're efficient," Springate contradicted him, "but . . . are we off the record on this one?"

"Sure."

"Can't trust the bastards."

"The leaks?"

"The goddam leaks." Springate puffed on the cigar, his brow furrowed with irritation. "They hate us."

Brody was surprised. "I've never heard that," he said.

"Well, it's true." Puff.

"What do you do about it?"

"Can't do a thing . . . result is, ministers are suffering from over-work." He pointed the wet end of the cigar at Brody. "Here's a quote for you: 'The whole trend of modern government is to increase the amount of detail with which departments have to concern themselves'."

Brody thanked him.

"Haven't you got anything to write with?" And when Brody shook his head: "This goddam 'new journalism'; I hate it."

"Sorry," murmured Brody.

"What else do you want to hear?"

"Tell me about the economy."

" 'The economy cannot assimilate the entire population'." Puff. Then, accusingly: "That was another direct quote."

"I'll try to remember it."

"What else. Ask me a question."

"How are the negotiations going with Washington concerning annexation?"

Springate rolled the cigar in his fingers; examined the ash, then took another draw. "Direct quote: 'This government has no inten-tion of petitioning the Americans for annexation'." He peered at Brody through the smoke. "All this is going on tape . . . " he

126

gestured toward his desk. " ... so I *know* what's on or off the record."

Brody nodded.

"Off-the-record?"

"Sure," Brody said.

"The U.S. doesn't want twenty-five million welfare-prone Canadians ... all voting the Democratic ticket." Suck, puff. The blue acrid haze was stinging Brody's eyes. "Ask me another; one that I can give you a direct quote."

"What are you doing about the foreign take-over of Canadian industry?"

"Direct quote: 'The government will continue its policy of selective investing in industries that are more than ninety per cent foreign corporate investment'."

"Jesus H. Christ!" exploded Brody.

Springate held the cigar out in front of him, eyeing Brody over the fire. "What's wrong with *you*?"

"Partial nationalization doesn't give the people of Canada control!"

Springate studied him, a growing dislike in his hooded eyes. "Who said anything about the people of Canada?"

"All that you've done with this buy-in program is create more government agencies for the corporations to capture."

"You don't like corporations?"

"I've never known one to put people before profit."

"It's too bad you feel that way." Springate put the cigar in his mouth, clamping it between his teeth and talking round it. Suspiciously he asked: "Are you sure you're a reporter?"

"No, I'm not a reporter," Brody said grimly. "I'm a concerned citizen."

It sounded farcical.

"Out," said Springate, heaving himself up from the sofa. "I don't have to talk to you."

Brody was on his feet. They stood glaring at each other. "Sit down," Brody ordered.

"Out," repeated Springate, a jab of cigar indicating the door.

When Brody refused the second time, Springate started for his

127

desk and phone. He ran into Brody's huge fist. The fist was wrapped up in Springate's suit. And since it was a well made suit, Brody's twisting grip turned it into a sort of straitjacket.

"I can't breathe," the Minister gasped. And he added, in choked amazement: "You're using violence."

Brody jerked the politician back and forth. "A Canadian citizen who uses violence," Brody said. "Surprise!"

"You'll hear from the Mounties about this," warned Springate. It was difficult talking over the wad of strained clothing under his chins.

"Sit down," Brody said firmly, guiding Springate backward to his former place on the sofa. "There."

When they were both sitting again, Springate said: "I warn you — whatever your name is — the Mounties . . . "

"The name is Brody," he interrupted, "and I've already heard from the Mounties . . . they put me in hospital."

"They did?" Doubtfully.

"Two broken ribs and a skull fracture," Brody said coldly. He nodded toward the window. "Right out front there."

"I never heard anything about it."

"That's the way you power brokers like your violence: invisible."

"What is it you want? What's your name?"

"Brody. It's a tough name; try to remember it."

"Can the sarcasm, Brody. What is it you want?" Springate had recovered his nastiness. With evidence of regret he leaned over and picked up the broken cigar which he deposited in the ashtray.

"Why can't the Cabinet — which is the way Canada is governed — solve the country's problems?"

"For Christ's sake!" Springate surged ahead to wag a finger under Brody's nose. "You don't even know *what* the Cabinet is!"

"It's the executive committee of the ruling class."

"You bastard!" Springate was furious with him.

"Why doesn't the Cabinet *do* something?"

"We perform on a very high wire . . . it's a long way to the concrete and no safety net."

"So?"

"You don't understand the saw-offs."

"Tell me about them."

"We're the party of Big Business."

"Both parties are," Brody amended.

Springate pursed his lips, then nodded. "Okay. Both parties are financially dependent."

"So where's the saw-off?"

"This is a business run country, Brody, are you aware of that?"

"Yes."

"If you'll allow me *that*, I'll point out that we are part of the U.S. business world. We're dependent."

"Maybe it's time we went on our own."

Springate shook his head emphatically. "Like it or not we're part of the American Empire."

"All we *have* to be is trading partners."

Springate shook a warning finger at him. "Not good enough. The U.S. must have a perpetual trade surplus; not only with us but with the rest of the world as well."

"Why?" It was a new thought to Brody.

"We might collapse the world's financial systems."

"To hell with that."

"Listen, Brody. The national interests of a country like Canada won't change, alter or supplant the global imperative of capitalism."

"Maybe it's time we got rid of capitalism."

"You're a deeply ignorant man," Springate said.

"Canada has enough resources left, and an educated population, to make it without the U.S."

"There's that 'Canadian nationalism' crap again. I'm sick of it."

"What's wrong with Canada first?"

"This nationalism hysteria that's plagued Canada has done enough damage to U.S.-Canada relations. We're trying for reconciliation."

"Reconciliation!?" Brody bellowed. "One side has the *power* and the other side gets reconciled to it."

"Of course, you bloody fool!" Springate shouted in his face. "That's what Canadians have known for two hundred years!"

Brody sat back. Perhaps 200 years of living next to aggressive Americans did breed a pussycat national character.

"Okay," Brody said slowly. "Maybe that's true. But today the United States is a declining world force. There's no reason Canada couldn't cut free now."

Springate seemed to feel better about him, for he leaned back. He looked tired. "We can't do that."

"Why not?"

"It's the saw-offs again." He smiled, more to himself than at Brody. "We're a business country; most of our business has to be done with the States."

"Why?"

"Our high costs of production freeze us out everywhere else."

"So you plan to keep selling our resources to the States? Buying them back in manufactured goods?"

"Look." Springate put his head back against the wall and closed his eyes. "That's not so bad. There's hardly a developing country in the world that isn't in that bag."

"Canadians don't think of Canada as a 'developing' country."

Springate opened his eyes. "Well maybe they'd better get used to the idea."

"A lot of Canadians don't think that way," Brody told him. "A lot of us want independence."

"And poverty?"

"Hard times, maybe," Brody allowed. "But a country with twenty-five million educated people, energy resources of its own," he paused, " . . . an industrial structure in place. Hell, we've got it made."

Springate sat up. "Those resources don't belong to us. They were developed by American capital."

"Forty years ago? Fifty?" Brody demanded. "How long do you allow the profits to flow out of the country before you reclaim the assets?"

Springate stabbed his stubby finger at him again. "That's treasonous talk!"

"What's treasonous about that?"

"Exports of resources gain a better deal for Canadian business in the American Empire."

"It's a bad deal," Brody said with flat conviction. "Lousy."

130

Springate stood up. "You used violence on me. Let me tell you about *real* violence."

"Go ahead."

"You just *try* that independence crap . . . just try taking Canada out of the American Empire. You'll have U.S. soldiers parachuting onto Parliament Hill. And they'll use napalm and nerve gas if they think they need it." His finger shook as he pointed at Brody. "They'll take us over!"

"They'll take us over anyway," Brody observed, "the way *you're* going."

"Annexation, if we can negotiate it, is more pleasant than a military occupation."

"Either way," Brody said to him, "it's violence against Canadians. The violence of exploitation, or the violence of the Pentagon."

"You can see our choice, Mister Brody." Springate was walking him hospitably to the door. "We are earnestly seeking a peaceful transfer of power: first, to Quebec as an independent republic; secondly, to Washington."

"We'll be another poor South, or an Appalachia," Brody forecast gloomily.

"Better than being a Vietnam."

"Neil Brody?" said the resonant voice on the phone. "I'm David Aardbard, CHOW-Radio, Ottawa."

"Yes?" Brody tried to recollect either Aardbard or CHOW. He couldn't.

"I host a late-night music and talk show."

"Yes?"

" 'Music for Insomniacs'?"

"Sorry," said Brody. "I sleep like a top."

"Ha ha ha," Aardbard laughed. It was a cultured laugh. "Between cuts I interview interesting people."

"You want to interview me?"

"Yes. I read the piece in the paper . . . 'The man who wants to save Canada'."

"I'd like to discuss it," Brody said firmly. He was so preoccupied with imagining what he'd say to the insomniacs that he failed to pay attention to the rest of it.

"I want to do the nostalgic trip back to the days of World War Two. Marlene Dietrich singing 'Lili Marlene', and all that."

"The history of the thing? Canada as a perpetual colony?" Brody asked.

"The great bombing raids; the fire storms over Ludwigshaven."

"Flak storms," Brody corrected absently.

"Churchill's famous 'White Cliffs of Dover' speech."

"We *could* discuss socialist alternatives," Brody suggested.

"Pardon?"

"Socialist alternatives for Canada?"

"Oh," chuckled Aardbard in his mellifluous voice. "No need to get into that. Ha ha ha."

Brody was fascinated with that laugh. "What day do you want me there?"

"Night, Mister Brody . . . 'Music for Insomniacs' is at night."

"Okay, night. What night?"

"Tomorrow, CHOW studios, eleven o'clock?"

"Sure," agreed Brody, "I'll be there at quarter-to."

The broadcast booth that Aardbard took him to was small, dirty and depressing. The double doors were padded with old acoustic tiles, which also lined the walls and ceiling. A single wide window looked into the control room where a young man presided over two turntables and a single bank of switches.

They sat on either side of a tiny table; between them was a microphone with a toggle switch in the base.

"When the red light goes on, we're on the air," Aardbard said to him nervously. Then he added: "I'm always nervous until I get on-air." Aardbard levered the toggle switch: "John? Will you give us ten seconds advance?"

"Okay," said a voice from an unseen speaker. The operator was looking at Brody through the glass as he spoke. "The news and sports will go first."

Brody nodded his thanks for the information.

Aardbard turned the switch off on the mike. He checked the wall clock, then drummed his fingers on the table. Brody felt claustrophobic.

"When the light comes on," Aardbard suddenly began explaining, "I'll introduce the show; John will spin the first disc and after it's over I'll introduce you."

"Will I just start talking?" Brody asked.

"Don't worry about that," Aardbard assured him. "I'll be asking you the questions."

"Long answers or short?" Brody was wondering if he shouldn't have supplied a list of suitable questions.

"You can answer them long," Aardbard said. "My listeners like the rambling narrative style."

The temperature continued to rise in the booth. Brody removed his jacket and hung it over the back of the chair.

Through the glass Brody could see a wall clock. It read 11:15 when the operator leaned ahead and pushed a switch on his console.

"Ten seconds to air." The disembodied voice made Brody jump.

Aardbard raised a hand in acknowledgement.

"Good evening, fellow insomniacs," Aardbard said with an unctuous smile at the mike. It was as if the microphone was a beloved insomniacal listener.

They sat for a few seconds in silence. Theme music swelled, then faded at a hand signal from Aardbard.

"It's Aard the Bard bringing you your nightly edition of . . . 'Music for Insomniacs'. Tonight we're taking a sentimental trip back through the years to the glory days of World War Two. We'll be hearing from those gold dust twins Bing Crosby and Bob Hope; the big band sounds; and a bit of nostalgia from our own Canadian entertainment industry: Bert Pearl and the Happy Gang.

"To get the evening underway," Aardbard cooed, "let's listen to Mart Kenny and His Western Gentlemen swing into 'When I Grow Too Old to Dream'."

They watched John flip the nearest turntable under the needle. Aardbard had a glisten of sweat on his brow; he looked as if he'd just earned his week's salary introducing this one show.

From his inner pocket Aardbard extracted a few pages of what turned out to be undecipherable notes; at least Brody was unable to make anything of them reading upside down. While the music was on Brody composed his thoughts.

"Mart Kenny, one of the all time Canadian great names. Is there *anyone* out there remembers dancing to Mart Kenny? Ha ha ha." Aardbard's question startled Brody. He remembered Mart Kenny very well.

"Tonight, I have with me as a special guest a man who does remember World War Two. He remembers it from the cockpit of a bomber high above the blacked-out cities of Europe. Here to share those memories is Neil Brody, a man whose medals made him famous." He paused, dramatically pointing at Brody. "Neil . . . what was World War Two *really* like?"

"Well!" spluttered Brody. "It was no bloody piece of cake!"

Aardbard looked alarmed. And when it appeared that Brody wasn't going to elaborate, he hastened to pick it up: "Piece of cake! Now there's an expression. What does it mean?"

"I came here to talk about saving Canada," Brody protested. "Not a damned war!"

"But this is a special program," Aardbard protested back. "You promised to talk about the war in the air. The last great days of glory for Canadian fighting men."

"Days of glory!?" shouted Brody. "A lot of good men getting their asses shot off!"

"Please!" soothed his host, his hands patting the air between them.

"I *won't* be quiet," Brody insisted. His voice continued rising. "Canada is going down the drain and you . . . you blithering idiot . . . want to talk about a war nearly half a century old."

Aardbard was no longer listening to him. The announcer was at the window, gesticulating at his operator who had, apparently, divined disaster and started another record. Aardbard headed for the door; he looked as if he were about to cry.

"I'm sorry . . . " Brody started.

His apology was cut off by the loudspeaker. "Station manager on the line, Aard. He's pissed off."

"Ooooh!"

Brody followed him out of the booth, and stood watching as the

134

frightened announcer picked up the phone. He figured Aardbard could do without his apology so he went back for his jacket and then headed down the hall to the side exit. He felt genuinely sorry.

The glass door led onto the small, almost empty, parking lot. The area was lit by the reflected glow of flood lamps on the exterior of the studio. The lamps illuminated the 8-foot high red letters 'CHOW' painted on the wall.

Brody hesitated, undecided whether to start walking home, or to wait for Jan. He knew she was listening to the program and would probably come to get him. Under the trees lining the nearby street was a police cruiser. Brody wondered if it was his surveillance. If it was, it was the first time the Mounties had used a car with rack lights and siren.

He decided to wait for Jan outside. As he stepped through the doorway a powerful arm locked round his neck from behind; from the sides, at the same instant, others pinioned his arms. There were, he realized as they forced him toward the parking area, at least five men.

The beating began at once. While three of them fought to hold Brody upright and immobile, the other two hammered him with boots and fists.

The shrill trill of a police whistle froze the action. Brody couldn't believe it. Neither, apparently, could the men holding him. "What the fuck's got into *him?*" panted the man behind.

Twee-eet! A shorter blast on the whistle. It came from the direction of the police car.

"Stay here you son of a bitch," said the voice in his ear.

Pain drove Brody to his knees as the man's knuckles gouged his kidney. The group left him for the police car. There was a brief discussion and then, as mysteriously as the recall, the men piled into the cruiser and drove away.

"Neil! Over here." Jan was standing behind a large figure in the deep shadows where the cruiser had been parked. As Brody drew near she asked him: "Are you all right?"

Brody recognized the man. Sergeant Godfrey. "What are *you* doing here?" Brody asked him.

"Don't get close to him, Neil," Jan warned.

135

"Have you got a gun?" he asked her.

"Right against his spine."

"That gun is illegal, you know," said Godfrey calmly.

"What do you want to do, Neil?" Jan asked him.

Brody spoke to Godfrey. "Are you prepared to leave us alone, Sergeant?"

"Yes, sir."

"Step away from him, Jan. Is this the way Mounties make their living nowadays, Sergeant?" Brody asked him.

"I don't make orders, sir . . . I just carry them out."

They stood holding each other while Godfrey walked to the CHOW studio and entered the door Brody had come out. He was apparently going in to use the phone. Brody felt weak. "Where's your car?" he asked her.

"On the next block."

She told him, as they walked, that the police car had passed her — lights flashing — on the way to the studio.

"I didn't realize it was you they were going for," she said. "But the program had barely started and there you were, shouting at the host . . . oh, Neil!" She squeezed his hand. "But they weren't ready for you to come out so soon."

"Where were you?" The pain in his back made talking difficult.

"I parked right behind the cruiser."

"What happened?"

"That Godfrey — is he the one who took your passport? — he came back and told me to move on. The rest of them were already running for the parking lot."

"The goon squad," Brody grunted. The pains made him gasp with every step.

She made him stop under a streetlamp. "Are you all right? You look awful."

"I'll be stiff tomorrow." He managed a smile for her concern.

When they were walking again she told him the rest of it. She'd parked the car and ran back.

"What about the gun control law?"

"Neil . . . when the government decided citizens couldn't have guns, *I* decided I might need one. I was thinking of the nights I walked home after evening sessions of the House." She paused: "But I never thought it would be to defend myself against my own government."

"Okay. What happened when you got back to the police car?"

"Godfrey was standing under the tree. You were just opening the door . . . so it was easy for me to step up and push the gun in his back."

"How did you convince him you were serious?"

"I was serious . . . he *knew* it." She stopped once again to face him. "Those . . . those, men . . . were beating you up. Oh, Neil!" She began crying.

"It's okay," he said, holding her close. "I'm okay."

"I told him to stop the beating . . . "

"Or you'd shoot?"

"I was leaning so hard he'll have a bruise on his backbone for weeks."

"I'm proud of you," Brody said. "Let's go home."

Later, in bed, Jan told him: "I never thought this kind of thing would happen in Canada."

"It happens everywhere, I guess. Canada isn't unique."

"Neil? I'm afraid they'll kill you."

"I don't think so," he said slowly. "I don't represent any real threat to anyone. I'm just a nuisance, I guess."

It was something they both wanted to believe.

Chapter 8

Brody sat at his desk looking out the window at a cool grey day. It wasn't raining, but it looked like it might. Down the street — he could see it by standing close to the window — was a surveillance car. Someone had put no-parking signs in front of the house so they'd have an unobstructed view. He wondered how many other people in Canada were getting this treatment.

The wrestling match with the Mountie goon squad had left him bruised and aching; his back was strained; he felt rotten. All he really wanted to do this morning was talk to Jan. He alternated between lying on the sofa and going through the newspapers for references to his ad of the week before.

Nothing; no editorial comment, no letters to the editor. He wondered whether the newspapers were suppressing letters that supported his views.

Lunch hour came and went; no Jan. He was worried by the time her car pulled into the driveway, and more worried when he saw her.

"What's wrong?" he asked, wrapping his arms round her. "You're shaking."

When they were sitting down she told him about the end of her political career. Her voice was tremulous with emotion. "Cabinet meeting," she said. "For once the boys were on time."

"What happened?"

"The P.M. handed me a letter." She was looking into his eyes; almost, but not quite, ready to cry. "It was my resignation."

"*Your* letter of resignation?"

"Ready for my signature."

"Did you sign it?"

"No."

"Good for you," he approved.

"Oh, Neil," she said, realizing he didn't understand. "They had already told the Press Gallery about it."

"Before you signed it? How did they know you'd agree to resign?"

Sudden tears glinted in her eyes.

"It didn't *matter* whether you signed it or not?"

She nodded, her cheek pressed against his chest.

Brody hesitated before asking: "Was it because of me?"

Her arms convulsed in a squeeze which sent pains shooting through his injured muscles. "Our relationship," she said, pushing back to look up at him. " 'Moral turpitude' . . . did you know that?"

He smiled at her. "I *love* you . . . is that 'moral turpitude'?"

"Know something, Neil?" she said. "Everything we say in this room goes onto tape."

"I'm not surprised. How do they do it?"

"From that car out there."

"I thought they were only watching us come and go."

"That too," she said. "Do you want to hear about the Cabinet meeting?"

"I thought you were sworn to secrecy."

She shook her head. "There's nothing secret about what I told those . . . "

"Yes?" he prompted, a tease in his voice.

"Those 'honourable' gentlemen." She laughed, and Brody was relieved.

Her mood changed back to serious. " 'For the good of the Party', the P.M. said. Which was all right," Jan affirmed.

"I don't think so," Brody disagreed. "You were the only Cabinet minister anyone could trust."

"Oh, Neil," she said, tears returning to her eyes. "You're such a babe . . . and I love you so much."

"Tell me what happened."

"It's not often that being the only woman in a gathering of men bothers me, but this morning was the worst."

Brody found himself getting angry.

"They seemed to be sitting there, just waiting to crucify me."

"Maybe they were."

"Maybe, come to think of it, they were." She thought, hard. "The security people have probably been feeding 'the scandal' into the P.M.'s office since the first night I spent with you."

"Most wonderful night of my life."

"You mean last night wasn't?"

"You got me," Brody said, chuckling at her jest. "Now tell me what happened this morning."

"They made me resign. But it's *you* they're worried about."

"Me?" Brody couldn't believe it. "My ad didn't bring so much as a letter to the editor."

"They're paranoid, Neil."

"What have they got to be paranoid about?"

"They don't trust the people; they're terrified of them." She paused, then: "They don't *understand* the people. They're afraid, desperately afraid, someone will emerge and say — as you are saying — 'Let's change the rules'."

Brody looked at her in partial disbelief. "They're afraid of a revolution?"

"Yes."

"That's why the Mounties are after us?"

"You, darling. They're trying to discourage *you*."

"Well," said Brody, speaking louder for the tape, "I can tell you they *have* discouraged me." And when they had smiled over that, he asked her: "Did you make a speech?"

"I did." Her tone became wistful. "Want to hear what I told my Cabinet colleagues?"

He squeezed her hand.

"I told them they are cowards, hypocrites, wafflers and ... "

"Bastards?" Brody suggested.

"They are," Jan said, "but I didn't think to call them that."

"What did you tell them?"

"I told them I was glad to be leaving the Liberal Party because of their spineless attitudes to the real problems of the country."

"Good girl," Brody encouraged.

"I told them their protect-the-wealth obsession should serve as the Party slogan."

Brody wished he could have been there.

"I told them their rape the resources, keep Canada as a hinterland ethic, was a crime against the nation."

"You're right," Brody agreed, admiration in his voice.

"Nothing's changed since the fur trade days."

"Did you tell them that?" Brody asked.

"No; but I told them their policies of making Canada a colony of the States was paralleled by their allowing Ontario to make colonies of the Prairies and the Maritimes."

"Good for you," he applauded.

"Do you think so?" She looked at him, then returned to the comforting circle of his arms. "Oh, Neil . . . I love you."

"Can we get married now?" he whispered into the halo of her hair.

She nodded. "Neil? I told them . . . just before I left . . . " She twisted in his arms to look at him full face. "If they kill you, they'd better kill me too; because anything you start will be finished by me."

Jan was in Toronto conferring with her riding executive the day Pete Ranallo and Karen Knudsen drove up in their old camper. Brody was delighted to see them. He shook hands with Pete and hugged Karen.

"How did you find me?" he asked, escorting them in.

"Hey, this is great!" Karen exclaimed, looking at the decor.

"Jan did it," Brody replied, then, unable to suppress his happiness: "We're going to get married."

"Oh, no!" chorused Pete and Karen.

"What's wrong?" Brody asked. "Aren't people allowed to get married any more?"

"Neil," said Karen, kissing him on the cheek. "We're happy for you."

"How did you find me?" he asked Pete again.

"Phoned the newspaper that carried your ad; told them I wanted to write to you."

"Good," Brody said. "I'm glad. What brings you to Ottawa?"

"You."

Brody was pleased. "If you're staying overnight," he said, "you can help us get married."

They agreed.

"Have you eaten?" Brody asked. "Can I make you sandwiches?"

His guests weren't hungry. Over a cup of tea Brody asked again the reason for the visit.

"It was your ad, Neil," Karen explained. "He hasn't quit talking about it since."

Pete may have been excited, yet he was calm when he put his proposition to Brody. "Let's team it," he said.

Pete's idea was to pool their talents. Brody would be spokesman, Pete would provide the backgrounding and co-ordination. "Ideas, Neil," he said, "we'll pool our ideas . . . and we'll scour the country for better ones." His dark eyes glowed with enthusiasm.

"The problem isn't 'ideas'," Brody said, thinking aloud, "it's implementing the ideas. That means 'organization'."

"That's where I come in," Karen said. "You men aren't the only members of this team."

"What are you going to organize?" Brody asked.

Karen looked determined. "There are two entire segments of the population that need organizing: women, and the old people."

"I don't see how . . . " Brody started to object.

"If Jan wants to join our team," Karen added, "she'd be a natural to organize the women."

Brody sat back, stunned with the magnitude of her idea.

Then he told them of Jan's forced resignation from the Cabinet, and of her decision to resign her Parliamentary seat as well. "She's in Toronto winding things up with her campaign chairman and the riding secretary." He looked at his watch. "Her plane is just taking off now."

"Are you planning to meet her?" Pete asked.

"No. She parked her car out there."

"Let's surprise her."

When Jan strode into the terminal, they were waiting. "What are *you* doing here!?" she cried. And it wasn't until after she'd given Brody an affectionate kiss that she welcomed Karen and Pete. "How are you?" She hugged them both. "What are you doing in Ottawa?"

On the way home Jan and Brody stopped for take-out chicken. When they'd gathered in Brody's apartment and were eating, they

142

told Jan what they'd been discussing: a team approach to the problem of organizing the people of Canada.

"You were talking about that *here*?" Jan asked Brody.

"So the place is bugged," Brody said. "So what?"

"You should have warned them: the Mounties are taping everything we say."

Pete shrugged. "They've been monitoring us, opening our mail, bugging our house . . . even my ecology school . . . for years."

"By the way," Jan asked, "what about your ecology school? Who's going to run it . . . and your farm . . . while you're away?"

Pete explained that a neighbour was watching the farm for them, and that he'd suspended classes indefinitely.

"What happens to Canada will probably be decided within two months," Pete said. "If Neil is willing to try, Karen and I will make one last effort for Canada too."

Karen added: "We know that as American immigrants we're stigmatized, but it's worth the try anyway."

"Well," Jan said, wiping her fingers on a paper napkin, "I don't think we should discuss anything more just now. I suggest we get out of here, at least for a while."

"We've got nothing to hide, Jan. We're not plotting treason," Brody protested.

"It's more than a point of principle between you and the government, darling. Other people are involved."

"Okay, what do you suggest?"

"I suggest we go for a drive in our camper," Karen offered.

"Is it bugged?" Brody asked jokingly. "I won't feel important if my words aren't being taped."

They spent the evening driving, stopping now and then on deserted roads.

"It embarrasses them," Pete said, referring to the police following them, "to look like idiots parked in the middle of nowhere watching us."

Pete's sardonic humour helped, but the police car was depressing. It made them feel like criminals; or conspirators. They resisted the

143

feeling and, for the moment at least, ignored the problem of police intimidation.

Out of that evening's talk was founded the 'People's Movement'. The four agreed to do their best, as long as they were financially able, to encourage the people of English-speaking Canada to opt for an independent nation; perhaps in association with Quebec, perhaps not.

"We aren't founding a political party," Karen summarized, "we're founding a movement to put power where it belongs in a democracy: with the people."

Jan pointed out that the People's Movement would, of necessity, evolve into a political party. "But whether it can progress that far in the time remaining is doubtful," she concluded.

They agreed to divide their efforts: Pete would handle the administrative end; Karen would try to organize the senior citizen groups; Jan would work with women's groups; Brody would try to reach the unemployeds.

"You might not have that much time," Pete told him. "I plan to keep you busy making speeches."

"To who?"

"University audiences; business clubs; service groups . . . anyone I can find that will pay for the privilege of hearing you."

"I don't think businessmen will want to listen to me."

"Oh yes they will," Pete said, "and they'll pay. We need those lecture fees to finance our newspaper." He turned to Jan. "Will you need help with your speeches?"

Jan smiled and shook her head.

"I won't need help either," Karen added. "I don't know if I can organize the old folks — they're so demoralized by pension red tape, malnutrition and everything — but I think I know what I want to say."

They ended by discussing the matter of the police spying on them. Since they couldn't prevent it, and since they felt their objectives were democratic, they decided to use Brody's room as their headquarters.

"We might as well expect police spies to join the Movement," Jan pointed out.

"Will we try finding them and kicking them out?" Karen asked.

"Hell, no," said Pete. "But let's keep reminding ourselves that everything that's said is being relayed to the nearest National Security desk."

They talked late into the night. When they returned to the city Pete dropped them at Jan's apartment; he and Karen would stay at Brody's. As they got out of the camper, he said to them: "Friday we hold the press conference."

The press conference to announce the People's Movement was held in the theatre of the National Press Building. Although it might have been considered a pseudo news event — something hoked up to attract free publicity — the presence of ex-Cabinet Minister Jan Stewart was news in itself.

The small theatre was only partially occupied when the four principals of the People's Movement followed the president of the Press Gallery onto the platform. They sat down on the chairs provided.

Bill Sturgess, Press Gallery president, sat to one side. Sturgess was a working member of the Gallery, elected by his peers for a one-year term of office. One of his duties was to act as chairman for press conferences, introducing the protagonists and umpiring questions from the floor.

"All right," said Sturgess, a TV newscaster with the looks and voice requisite, "let's get things under way."

The audience quieted; the lights of the theatre dimmed; the stage lights came up.

"We have with us four people, one of whom you know: Jan Stewart, until recently a Cabinet minister with the present government. The other three are . . . " Sturgess glanced at the envelope on which he had jotted their names, "Ms. Karen Knudsen; Professor Pietro Ranallo; and Mister Neil Brody.

"The group on the platform have started something called the 'People's Movement'. I leave it to Mister Brody to explain what it is about. I don't know whether each of our guests is to make a statement . . . " he looked at Jan who nodded, " . . . each of the four will make a brief statement. Then we'll follow with questions. Mister Brody?"

"Ladies and gentlemen," Brody began. "You are all members of the news gathering profession . . . I have no need to describe to you Canada's melancholy situation." He paused, then: "You probably know more about the situation than I do."

"Then why are you here?" asked a voice from the audience.

"Go ahead, Mister Brody," said Sturgess.

"Canada is in a perilous state," Brody began once more. "Quebec is about to leave us; a third of the work force is on the streets; inflation rides upward each year."

Saying these things brought his bitter feelings to the fore and his voice grew stronger as he told them the capitalist system was degenerating and that a right wing mentality had taken over. It was brought on, according to Brody, by the increasingly repressive measures taken to control the disaffected poor people and the technologically displaced educated people.

In flat, uncompromising terms he told the journalists that "government action — or 'non-action' . . . " had forced small groups such as teachers and hospital workers to confrontation tactics; and that the government had used these as excuses to invoke stronger measures. "This is where the Civil Unrest Act came from," Brody declared.

He told the skeptical news men and women that Canadian police forces had assumed extra-legal powers and that the public didn't protest since it was being done in the name of protection.

"Who protects us from the crimes of government?" Brody asked. "Who punishes the crimes of industry? The monopoly practices . . . cartels . . . price rigging?"

And he told them what they were also seeing in Canada was civil disorder. "It's in the form of petty crime, vandalism, muggings . . . crimes by poor people *against* poor people.

"This is desperation crime," Brody said with pent up fury, "and it will continue to increase."

He strode to the edge of the platform. "I suppose you think I'm here to announce a solution to the problems; I am not.

"The problems -- poverty; unemployment; crime; urban and rural decay — have been developing in Canada for decades.

146

"Solutions to the problems . . . lots of solutions . . . instant cures . . . have been brought out by our leaders, regularly."

Brody's natural dignity, his honest outrage, made him a compelling figure. "I think it's tragic, and disgracefully wrong, that *all* of these alleged solutions deal with the structures of society . . . and none with what society is: the people!"

Again he paused, looking at his bored audience, only some of whom were bothering to take notes. "The hope for the future of this country does not lie with governments — with more legislation; with more regulatory agencies — it lies with the people."

Brody's voice dropped to normal tones. "The solution *always* lies with the people. The People's Movement," his gesture took in the four of them, "has one purpose: to awaken the Canadian people from the apathy that has allowed the present situation to evolve." He sat down.

The chairman/host said: "We'll now hear from Jan Stewart."

"Thank you, Bill," she said with an easy familiarity. "My colleague, Neil Brody, is also my husband. We were married yesterday."

Notebooks that had gone unused were suddenly snapped open; ballpoints were now zigging across the pages. A voice from among the scribblers intoned: "Congrat's."

"Thank you," Jan said to the unidentified well wisher.

"I'd like to say at the outset — to save question time later — that my decision to join the People's Movement was not motivated by, or connected with, my resignation from the government last week. Okay?" Her smile was sunny.

"We originators of the People's Movement don't know exactly where it will lead. We are not a political party; we *are* reformers.

"We feel, as my husband has just expressed it, that the Canadian people can and must take responsibility for their own country.

"We think it obvious that the economic system of North America has failed.

"We think that with the break up of Confederation, the time has come for Canadian citizens to decide — for themselves — what is to be done."

While Jan was talking, Brody noticed that none of the TV cameras were manned; nor was the recording booth in use. The broadcast media were not interested in the People's Movement.

"Canadians are the world's most politically alienated people," Jan continued. "Less than thirty per cent of the electorate bothered to vote in the last federal election.

"In the face of such alienation — I know you are thinking this, that's why I mention it — you are wondering how we hope to change apathy into action.

"We propose to use the group system; the team. I wonder how many of you will refer to it as 'the communist cell structure'?"

She laughed, and all the ballpoints paused; no need to scribble a laugh. "The team can be any number of people, not exceeding ten. When the eleventh person joins a group, a new one is formed."

"What are they going to do?" someone in the audience called out.

"We don't know," Jan answered. "We only know what our team is going to do."

She told them of the plan.

"I don't know what will become of this," Jan concluded. "I can only tell you that it has started."

There was a stirring in the audience as the chairman introduced Karen.

"Karen Knudsen, a former social worker in Chicago, now a Canadian citizen."

"Thank you," Karen said. Her lithe figure and tanned blonde beauty assured her of attention.

"Since Mister Sturgess mentioned my social work background, I'd like to comment on that profession.

"Social work is a big sham: a put on, and a lie.

"There are many earnest, educated people who enter the field with the desire to help." Her lovely smile was sardonic. "They don't."

Karen explained that the profession existed solely to help poor people cope with rotten life situations. "The one thing that might help the poor — money — is the one thing our money society is not about to give them.

"The poor are said to be incapable of managing their own affairs; so they are 'social worked' to adapt to the discipline of our industrialized society.

148

"They can't make it — for varied reasons — so they are shunted off with the others excluded from the economic system. I'm speaking of the aged, the sick, the handicapped . . . the young people and the old people; the unemployed people."

Karen's voice was vibrant with emotion. The audience sat, mesmerized. "Unemployed and unemployable," she went on. "And since they are *not* on someone's payroll and *cannot*, therefore, pay taxes . . . our society consigns them to the most meagre levels of existence.

"The hungry are given nutritional advice instead of food. Our old age pensioners have to shoplift groceries. This is Canada!"

Karen stood, silent for the moment. "Our governments, our leaders, have had ample time to solve the problems. They never have; they are never going to. That's why we've started the People's Movement.

"Something enormous is dying," she said. "Capitalism? I don't know. But an old system is dying.

"Independent of any present political will, a new society is coming." She sat down.

Unexpectedly, for journalists prize their cynicism, there was a spatter of applause.

"Professor Ranallo, formerly with the Biology Department of Carleton University . . . "

"Toronto," Pete corrected with a smile.

"I'm sorry . . . formerly of U of T."

"They got rid of me," said Pete.

Since the purge of American professors was now viewed as a blot on Canada's history, Pete's remark drew a laugh.

"Karen mentioned the sham of social work. I'd like to mention another one: the one person one vote sham. It's a sham as long as the rich can buy political influence.

"I guess that's the real reason there has to be a People's Movement."

He started on a new tack, telling them that many people claimed today's situation was no worse than it had been in the 1930s. "But in that depression even the employed had very little," Pete said.

Today, he went on, Canada's political leaders extolled the

149

national average income which had doubled several times since the thirties. "No one mentions that each time it doubles . . . the spread between the employed and the unemployed quadruples."

Pete let the point sink in. He continued: "On the streets today the unemployed person meets tradesmen, technicians, and the professionally-trained . . . all of them relatively wealthy people . . . "

He didn't get to finish the thought.

"A third of a million jobs going begging!" jeered someone in the audience.

Pete pointed in the man's direction. "There *are* jobs! But *you* don't want them and you won't take them . . . you can't live on the pay."

When the heckler failed to respond, Pete went on: "We've already got a de facto totalitarian system," he said. "Canada has more controlling legislation on the books than any other western country."

" 'Love us or leave us'," carolled another heckler. It brought a laugh.

"Well, okay," Pete said when the laughter died. "But I think you just illustrated the problem: people like you don't care."

The theatre was silent.

"You people have jobs; most of you work for conglomerate media interests; you command good salaries . . . "

"Bull-*shit*!" said his heckler sotto voce.

"Nevertheless," Pete shot back, "you people have a decent income. You have security. You can afford the personal choices that make life interesting.

"You're prepared to leave social decisions to our political and economic elites," he challenged them.

"Why not?" demanded an irritated voice.

"Precisely," Pete said. "Thank you."

He stroked his beard while everyone thought of what had just happened. "Your attitude makes you part of the problem . . . " Pete started to say.

"What problem?" interjected the heckler.

"The problem of the alienation of the working classes; the employed *and* the unemployed."

No response.

150

"You people are securely on the side of the Establishment. Why not? Everything you have of the 'good' life you owe to your employers who are capitalists . . . and charter members of Canada's Power Elite.

"And I'm aware of the restrictions under which you are obliged to work. I know, for instance, that even if all of you file news stories on what transpires here today . . . very little of it will appear in print."

"So what's your problem?" the heckler tried again.

"Not only *my* problem," Pete answered. "*Your* problem. You don't understand the working classes; you can't relate to the unemployeds; to the impoverished farmers; or to those other groups Karen mentioned." Pete abruptly sat down.

"A-a-ah." The surprised chairman had just violated the announcer's code. "Are we ready for questions?"

Pete's baiting was bound to provoke the audience. Three of them were on their feet before the stage lights went out and the theatre lights came up.

"One at a time," Sturgess instructed, "and address your question to the person you want to answer it." He pointed at a tall caved-in older man. "Alex?"

"My question would be to Mister Brody . . . assuming he is the leader of this so-called 'People's Movement'. Would he tell us just where it happens to fit in the political spectrum?"

Brody didn't care for the sarcasm. As the man folded into his chair, Brody got up. "The solutions to Canada's problems lie with the people," he said. "I suppose you'd call that a socialist principle. I don't care what label you tie onto Truth . . . it remains the truth."

"You didn't answer my question."

"Oh," said Brody. "I'm sorry. Neither the Conservatives nor the Liberals *can* learn nor *will* learn. They are both liberal in rhetoric, traditional in outlook, expedient in practice. Our People's Movement will be something entirely new." Brody sat down.

Reporters were on their feet, trying for the attention of the chairman. Sturgess pointed at a woman. "Sally."

"My question is to Jan Stewart," she said in a clear and forceful voice. "In view of the failure of each and every movement this country has ever known — I refer to the Women's Liberation Movement; the Ecology Movement; the Farmers' Protest Movement, as examples — what reason do you have for thinking your People's Movement will be any more successful?"

"Sally . . . you've asked an unanswerable question. Neither I nor my colleagues know whether the People's Movement will succeed.

"The people of Canada are terribly divided. In part, this has been a deliberate and tragic policy of successive federal governments.

"The reason has been, quite simply, exploitation.

"The Indians — in the first place — then the immigrants; the women; the labouring classes. Today it's the farmers; the white collar workers; small businessmen and, of course, ordinary working men and women."

Brody marvelled at Jan's ability with words. Once started on a sentence she never hesitated.

"You can see," Jan concluded, "how the free enterprise, exploit thy neighbour ethic would divide these groups.

"This is what has happened, and this is what we are up against."

"Okay," Sturgess said. "Howard, go ahead."

"I have a question for anyone," said a tousled youth with rolled up magazines sticking out of his jacket pockets. "Why is it that community action groups always fail?"

"Most groups fail," Karen said, standing up, "because the educated middle class people take over the leadership function. I'm talking about large city, working-class neighbourhoods."

As before, Karen's beauty and intensity of expression rivetted everyone's attention. "It is often *these* people who organize community action groups in the first place. And they love it! The meetings; the late night talks; the delegations to City Hall; the pamphlets and the letters to editors."

Karen skewered her audience with a curved finger. "But it doesn't have a damn thing to do with the realities of the people who must work!"

She needed a second to control her feelings. "The meetings are boring for the working-class people," Karen continued, "they have to go to work the next day . . . not prepare a lecture for a class next week.

152

"And all the emotional talk about confrontation, deals being cooked up with this politician or that one, worry them. Finally they say to-hell-with-it and quit attending.

"That's why," Karen concluded, "community action groups always fail."

"Just a second," the chairman said to one man, "Phil Croll has been trying to get a question in . . . Phil?"

"A question for Professor Ranallo." The questioner was short, fat and intense behind thick glasses.

"Go ahead," Pete told him.

"This People's Movement thing sounds like yet another call for 'Workers Control'. Would you care to comment on that, sir?"

"Sure," said Pete. "I might point out that people like us, discussing questions like these — making policy for the working classes, as it were — is just what the working classes don't want and don't need.

"So the straightforward answer to your question would be: no . . . the People's Movement is not 'yet another call for Workers control'.

"All we're proposing is that ordinary people band together in groups of ten or less, and discuss what needs to be done."

"That's a very simplistic answer to my question," the short man protested. "What about the workers seizing control?" He sat down.

"Mister!" Pete was pointing at the man, so angry his finger trembled. "Don't talk about workers 'seizing control'. There isn't going to be any of *that*."

Pete glared at the reporter who slid deeper into his chair. "Not that workers shouldn't have control — they damn well should!" Pete lowered his hand. "But there would be a blood bath if they tried.

"This government — any capitalist supportive government — is not going to allow the workers to revolt . . . to 'seize control' in your words."

Agitated, Pete began pacing his corner of the platform. "Back in 1970," he reminded, "they called out the army to put down a revolution which totally consisted of the kidnapping of one diplomat and one politician.

"I said 'blood bath' if the workers revolted, and that's just what I meant. The police, the army, the security forces which now make Canada a government-armed camp would shoot to kill anyone who stepped out of line so far as to suggest 'seizing control'."

Pete, still glowering at the questioner, finished: "Forget *that* kind of talk. That's not what the People's Movement is about."

Pete stalked back to his chair and sat down. His outburst had chilled the proceedings.

"Are there any more questions?" asked the chairman.

A young woman stood up; she looked like a high school student to Brody. "Could I ask Mister Brody just what he sees as his purpose?"

"Purpose?" Brody asked her. "You're asking me what I want?"

"Yes," said the girl.

"What I want . . . what I'd like to see," Brody said slowly, "is a world based on a morality of mankind." He smiled at the girl before adding: "But since that seems unlikely, and since I live right here in Canada . . . I want to see our country a place where the worth of the individual is recognized."

The girl appeared to want to ask another question but the chairman interceded. "Bill Baker?"

Baker was tall; tinted glasses hid his eyes. "I'd like to ask these people what they intend to do about the problem of regionalism in this country." The man seemed satisfied that he'd asked the ultimate question in Canadian studies.

Brody rose to answer. "The People's Movement is founded on this premise: that every problem has a solution. And that ordinary people — working together — can solve their own community and regional problems."

"Give me an example of one of your ideas for solving regional problems," Baker insisted.

"Okay," said Brody. "For example: imports from the States equal sixty per cent of the value of goods produced in Canada.

"Have you any idea of what the U.S. allows in? Two per cent!

"I suggest we follow the lead of our American friends and reduce our imports of manufactured goods to the same percentage: two per cent."

"But that would just raise the prices here in Canada," protested

Baker. "We can't compete with the mass market advantage of the States."

"That," Brody said, "is nonsense. We would instantly create a domestic market worth eighteen billion dollars."

Brody leaned forward. "Can you imagine how many jobs *that* would create in Canada?"

"It still wouldn't affect the problems of the regions," Baker argued.

"You're wrong!" Brody's strong voice made everyone jump. "The manufacturing and industrial plant required to service our own market could be regionally established." He shook his head at the man. "It doesn't *have* to be concentrated in a tiny corner of Ontario."

"Okay," interrupted the chairman. "We have time for one more question." He looked round the theatre. A few languid hands hung in the air. "Miss . . . ?" he didn't know her name. "Your question?"

"Wouldn't this People's Movement accelerate Canada toward the communist example?"

Brody was about to reply when he noticed Pete stirring in his chair. "Would you like to answer this one?" Brody asked him.

Pete bounded to his feet. "Two or three quick points to your question about communism," Pete told the girl. "First: although the People's Movement *is* socialist oriented, it won't be part of the Canadian Left which has thoroughly alienated itself from the people.

"Secondly: there is no country in the western world that would adopt the socialist ideal."

Pete hesitated, fighting the impulse to elaborate. He won. "Thirdly," he said, "it is the corporations themselves that are moving the western world toward convergence with the communist example.

"The vertically integrated company that plants forests, tends them, harvests them, transports and processes the wood, distributes and markets the products, employs thousands. And they work in a bureaucratic maze as complex and as rigid as anything you'd find in communist countries."

Pete stood for a moment, waiting for the girl to respond. When she didn't, he sat down.

"One last question . . . " the chairman said. "Bill Baker?"

The man who had argued with Brody earlier read from a slip of paper. "Mister Brody, could you tell us about your dispute with the Income Tax people?" He looked up. "Something to do with your bankruptcy?"

Brody was astounded. Before he could reply Sturgess intervened: "I don't think the question has much to do with the subject," he told Baker. "On behalf of the Press Gallery I'd like to thank our guests for being with us this morning."

As the reporters were leaving, Pete asked: "Could we remain here awhile? We'd like to talk things over."

"Sure," Sturgess agreed. "If anyone wants the room they'll ask you to leave. Good luck," he added.

"I don't owe the Income Tax anything!" Brody protested when they were alone.

Pete looked at him. "Don't worry about it," he said.

"Don't worry about it!" sputtered Brody.

"It's a standard tactic."

"What is? Why?"

"The government is trying to discredit you."

"But I don't *owe* any tax."

Pete spoke to Jan. "I'd have thought it was premature of the government to counterattack just yet."

"They're paranoid," she said. "Neil's visit to Dan Springate was inflated into a Cabinet crisis."

"Okay," said Pete. "They're going to overreact. We might as well be prepared for it. Jan . . . I'd guess you'll be the next to get it."

"Yes. They'll smear me too, if they can . . . and I imagine they can."

Karen told them: "Everyone involved with the civil rights and war protests went through this in the States. We just have to be patient."

"There's something we have to face," Pete warned. "It happened with the anti-war, *and* the civil rights movement: 'patience' may mean 'defeat'."

156

Chapter 9

The day after their press conference Pete bought a folding table and a bulletin board. Brody's room was now People's Movement headquarters.

The plan for Monday morning was local recruiting by Jan, Brody and Karen, while Pete stayed at the office lining up speaking engagements.

"It's grass roots stuff," Pete told them, "but nobody's going to provide us with a national platform."

"We had that last week," said Jan ruefully, pointing at the news clipping on the otherwise bare bulletin board. It represented the total impact of their press conference.

OTTAWA (CP) — Jan Stewart, a former Cabinet minister of the Liberal government, who last week resigned her seat in Parliament as well, has resurfaced as a founding member of the People's Movement.

At a sparsely attended Ottawa press conference Friday, the four organizers said the purpose of the movement is collective action to solve the country's problems.

They would organize Canadians in groups of ten citizens, similar to the communist cell structure system used during subversive stages of the Party's development.

Ms. Stewart announced, at the start of the press conference, her marriage to Neil Brody, also a principal in the new movement.

Brody is an elderly eccentric now living in Ottawa. His background includes a failed business, tax evasion, and flirtations with various radical

While Karen visited a senior citizen home on the outskirts of
Ottawa, Brody and Jan went to the taxation office.

"I'll be right back," Brody told her.

At the tax enquiry counter the man told Brody his file had been
'pulled'; that it was just 'routine'; and that if anything was amiss
he'd hear from them.

"When?"

"I don't know," said the man.

Through a nearby window Brody noticed a police cruiser pull up
in the parking spot next to Jan. He ran for the stairs.

When he got there he saw a Mountie hand Jan's purse back to
her.

"Thank you, Constable," she said evenly.

"What do *you* want?" Brody demanded.

The Mountie ignored him, heading for the cruiser.

"What was *that* for?" Brody asked her.

"I think he was looking for my gun."

"Did he *say* he was looking for a gun?"

"Of course not." She started the engine. "Come on, Neil, there's
no one to complain to anyway."

They reached the Chinese Embassy in time for the hand-out
ceremony. As they walked toward the line up Brody recognized the
sandy-haired man he'd spoken to before.

"Hi," Brody said, extending his hand like a political hopeful, "I'm
Neil Brody." They shook hands. "This is Jan Stewart, my wife."

"Ron Taylor," replied the man with an engaging smile. "Unemployed engineer," he explained about himself, then indicated the
rest: "Fair number of engineers here."

The people around moved closer to hear what was being said.

"Here come the cops," someone said anxiously.

158

"It's okay," Jan reassured them. "They're following us." Then she added in a clear voice: "They think we're here to corrupt you. Convert you to socialism."

That brought a laugh.

"Start corrupting me," said someone.

Another laugh.

With two unwelcome Mounties taping his words from the edge of the gathering Brody told them about the People's Movement.

"What do we do with the ideas we come up with?" Ron Taylor asked. "Keep in mind we have no money."

"*Nobody* has any money," Brody affirmed. "But keep in touch with us." And he gave Taylor his address and phone number.

"Ron?" Someone in the crowd expressed a common sentiment: "I wouldn't get involved."

Brody looked in the direction of the voice. "That's been our Canadian attitude for the past forty years . . . and look where you're standing today: in a bread line."

"It's okay for you, mister. You haven't got kids. You aren't hungry. You aren't *us*."

Brody knew it, and was ashamed. "I apologize," he said.

In addition to talking to the group at the Chinese Embassy, they had solicited support in beer parlours, pool rooms, and at a government construction site. They weren't allowed on-site but they did well with the unemployeds who stood outside the hoardings watching the trucks and the overhead crane. It was almost too noisy to converse.

"It's all automation," an older man told them. "They don't need us." And he added: "That's the problem."

"The solutions to the problems lie with the people," Brody told him, grateful for the cue.

And because Brody had the worker's weathered look, they felt at ease. They were interested in what he had to say. Jan's presence was an added attraction, and they talked to her too.

It was late afternoon when they started back. Brody noticed Jan watching her rear-view mirror. "Forget them," he advised her, but the persistence of the police was depressing him too.

When they arrived at headquarters Ron Taylor held the door open for them.

"Well, hello!" Jan said in surprise.

Standing in the line-up only took part of his day, Ron explained. The rest of his time was free. "I might just as well get involved," he said cheerfully.

They discussed the day's events. Things had not gone well for Karen. Mounties had stopped her, demanding a 'certificate of mechanical worthiness' for the camper. She was told to get one within 48 hours or it would be impounded.

"That wasn't all," Karen added. "They followed me, and when I went to leave, the camper wouldn't start."

"What did you do?" Jan asked.

"I went over to the police car and asked them to help me . . . they refused and laughed," Karen said.

"Those bastards," Brody murmured.

"I saw a man cutting the lawn," Karen continued, "so I asked him for help. Guess what? Someone had pulled the distributor wire for me."

"Okay," said Pete. "That's it." He turned and put his arms around her. "Where you go, I go too."

Ron offered a solution and it was accepted: he would man the office in the afternoons, freeing Pete to accompany Karen.

"You didn't hear about my stage hands," Karen told them.

On her way back to headquarters she'd noticed six strikers on a picket line behind the National Arts Centre.

"No one would see them *behind* the Centre," Jan remarked.

"It's the only place the police would give them a permit to march," Karen explained.

"Were they interested in the People's Movement?" Jan asked.

"They formed a group as soon as I suggested it."

"So would *I*," Pete teased, "if a gorgeous woman like you asked me."

After dinner Pete told them of his telephone progress. "I've got Neil speaking engagements at two universities: Queen's and Toronto. Also . . . " satisfaction was in Pete's voice, " . . . the American Empire Club . . . Thursday noon."

160

"Wha-at?" Brody couldn't believe it.

"Sheer coincidence," Pete told them happily. "I phoned the secretary just when he was tearing his hair over a replacement speaker."

"Did you tell him what Neil will be talking about?" Jan asked.

"The Club wants controversial speakers . . . he said a socialist topic would be welcome."

They applauded Pete's effort.

"Thank you," he said, bowing. "You want to hear about Jan's schedule?"

Jan was to address the Professional Women's Institute one evening, and the Women Against Men the next day. Both groups were located in Toronto.

"What about me?" Karen asked.

"You . . . have a meeting with the executive of the Pension Power activists, Thursday afternoon."

"Do I get to hear Neil's speech to the American Club?"

"Of course . . . we all do."

All but Ron, who would stay at headquarters in Ottawa.

"What are we doing with the ideas the different groups send in to us?" Ron asked Pete.

"We have to collate them — package them somehow — and get them back out to the groups."

"This is a publicity problem, isn't it?"

"We need some kind of newsletter," Pete said, "but that leaves the problem of distribution."

"What about a publications permit?" Jan interjected.

Pete was brought up short; it was something he hadn't thought of.

"She's right," Ron told them. "Anything printed for public distribution requires a permit."

No one believed the government would grant it.

"Can we use the mails?" asked Karen.

It was Jan who answered. "The Post Office might just compile a list of names and addresses for the Mounties. We could be endangering a lot of good people."

Pete's eyebrows were a horizontal line of worry. "What do you think?" he asked her.

"I'd say: use the mails; we have to: it's only your newspaper that's illegal."

"We *need* a newspaper," Pete insisted.

"Leave it with me," Ron said. He found the other four staring at him. He laughed and quoted: " 'The solution lies with the people'."

"Are you going to give us a hint?" Pete asked.

"Not yet . . . just leave it for me . . . and the people."

Pete saved his own good news for the last: he was to address a Faculty Club luncheon at Carleton University the coming Wednesday.

The next morning Brody telephoned Sgt. Godfrey at Mountie headquarters. He spoke rapidly, keeping his anger under control.

"I never thought I'd have occasion to speak to you again, Sergeant, but I want to protest the harrassment of your surveillance teams. Canada is still — nominally, perhaps — a democratic country. Squad cars of police following . . . "

Godfrey interrupted with a reminder of the provisions of the Civil Unrest Act.

"Where's the 'civil unrest'?" demanded Brody. "We're a group of concerned citizens trying to effect democratic reform in a democratic country!"

Godfrey promised to speak to his personnel about interference with citizens' rights, but concluded: "I have no authority to terminate the L.W."

"The *what*?"

"Our 'listening watch', Mister Brody. The government's obligation and right to monitor what's going on. Good day, sir."

The luncheon was held in the dining room of the faculty lounge. While Pete sat at the head table beside the president and host; Brody, Jan and Karen shared a table in a far corner. The meal — served by uniformed waitresses — the settings, and the lounge itself, gave Brody the idea that professors were better cared for by society than anyone.

The faculty members attending bothered Brody. They seemed to be physical nothings. They had the look of vested authority, a look of haughty disdain. The whole scene irritated him.

"Darling," Jan squeezed his hand, "try not to be so restless."

"I don't like it here."

"I know; but your antagonisms are showing."

Brody had to laugh. He was glad that it was Pete addressing these highbrows.

Tink-tink-tink-tink! The president was rapping his water glass with his spoon. It was time for Pete's talk.

Pete was a superb speaker. He told the professors that Canada's intellectuals had let the country down. That the universities were cultural ghettos; cloisters; equivalents to medieval hermitages. He said academics were monks, strolling the garden paths of Canada's campuses, meditating on their curricula vitae while outside the monastery walls secular tyranny had taken over.

"It's happening!" Pete said in ringing tones. "Capitalism is demanding the stabilizing support of a total political power and you people are prepared to let it happen."

Pete said that intellectuals — as the most highly educated of Canadians — carried a special responsibility of leadership. But the leadership in thought had never been forthcoming.

"The treason of the intellectuals," Pete told them, "is based on the bureaucratic establishment of your cultural existence." His imperious gesture took in the faculty lounge. "You have it too soft!"

Pete's closing words were, for Brody, an emotional wringer.

"We are free men and women," Pete said in quiet tones. "We are *free*.

"Now ... today ... we must take our heritage seriously. We must point out the perils that threaten Canada ... and we must do it now!"

Pete's sensitive eyes scanned an audience that was implacably hostile to him. "As intellectuals," Pete said, "we've got to forget about our own alienation. Forget it long enough to write radical critiques ... to devise new programs ... to present to Canadians arresting views of the future.

"If *we* don't do these things ... " he concluded, "who will?"

The applause was perfunctory. Brody realized, with a feeling of frustration, that the Carleton faculty members were unimpressed with Pete's appeal.

A man stood up on the far side of the room. "I find it slightly strained that you, Professor Ranallo, an American citizen and by definition a cultural imperialist, should be telling Canadian academics what *we* should be doing."

Brody thought Pete would tell them of his Canadian citizenship. He didn't.

"You people got rid of American teachers; 'cultural imperialists' in your phraseology. Did it make any difference? Was there a flowering of Canadian intellectual thought?"

His sarcasm was withering.

"Did you improve the calibre of instruction? Or was it just nationalistic featherbedding?

"Your anti-Americanism is a pain," he told them. "The only dynamism Canada has ever known came from the States . . . from the United Empire Loyalists to right now."

Pete surveyed the room, his contempt showing. "I know the strengths of the Canadian character," he said. "But they aren't to be found in your universities . . . where the students are spineless and the teachers have no balls."

Pete sat down. The perfect silence was destroyed by Brody's enthusiastic bellow: "Bloody fine speech, that!"

The head table was on a platform two feet higher than floor level. It meant that Brody and the others who climbed up there could look down on the round tables where 300 members of the American Empire Club chatted their way through a four course meal.

An oblong table to one side had a placard 'Press' on it. Among the journalists sitting there was a Mountie. He was there to record Brody's speech. His microphone was taped to the stem of the mike which Brody would be using.

The cheerful clink of cutlery punctuated the buzz of countless conversations in a room full of happy, chatting people. Near the back of the convention hall were Jan, Karen and Pete. They had a table to themselves. They seemed to be enjoying their meal, and each other's company. Brody was depressed.

164

"Anything wrong with your meal, Mister Brody?" asked the president of the Club.

"No . . ." Brody couldn't remember the man's name. "I'm just nervous about my speech."

"Don't be," the amiable president told him. "*I* used to be nervous . . . look at me now."

Over the coffee — and before the speech — the president asked him for some background for his introduction. "You're a socialist, I understand," said the president, scribbling the word on his napkin.

"People's Movement, anyway," Brody agreed.

The president wrote 'people's movement', but left 'socialist' on top. "Which university degree do you normally mention?" asked the president, beaming at him.

"I don't have one."

"You don't? How surprising." He jotted 'self-made' on the napkin. "In what field did you make your fortune?" The pen remained poised.

Considering all the things Brody wasn't, the president made a creditable introduction. "Mister Brody is one of the founding principals of the People's Movement," he concluded, "a new organization devoted to the independence of Canada."

Since the audience was made up of businessmen — and since Pete had advised: " . . . tailor your speech to the interests of your audience" — Brody opened by discussing capitalism.

"The capitalist economy is destroying our capitalist civilization," Brody told them.

And awhile later: "Businessmen are building a collective society for private profit."

And again: "If the multi-nationals are as beneficial as claimed, then Canada — dominated by foreign corporations to a far greater degree than any other developed country — should have the strongest economy in the world.

"Instead . . . we have the highest unemployment rate, and the highest rate of inflation . . . in the developed world."

His speech was unencumbered with notes or outline. One thing reminded him of another. His mention of the internationals led him to conjecture about corporations in general.

"It's not at all clear," Brody said in a voice full of earnest doubt, "by what right the corporation is entitled to power at all."

And he finished that line of thought with: "Large corporations do not go bankrupt."

His audience was unresponsive.

Brody forged ahead, explaining that once corporations gained control of entire markets they no longer had to fear the blight called 'Competition'. This kind of control, Brody said, represented power. And this thought led him to talking about the power of corporations to set their own levels of profit.

This, he told them, is a form of violence. He went on: "You probably think violence is guns and war; maybe a revolution." His voice grew louder as his anger increased. Soon he was shouting.

"Violence is inflation that exceeds twenty per cent per year!

"Violence is fourteen per cent mortgages!

"Violence is three hundred per cent increase in food prices!

"Violence is thirty-seven per cent of the work force on the streets!

"Violence . . . " Brody paused to glare at his restive audience, "is hunger and slums, poverty and disease." He paused once again, then added: "It's corporations paying less tax than the poor people; corporations rigging markets; corporations collapsing regional economies because of an adverse profit picture."

Several of the audience were wending their way through the tables toward the door. Jan gave him a finger and thumb circle of encouragement. He continued in calmer tones.

He told them that while corporate violence and government violence are invisible, the violence of the ordinary people was very visible because it was practiced on one another.

He explained that governments employ thousands of functionaries — lawyers, judges, wardens . . . police, guards and parole officials — to administer what Brody called 'social violence'.

"So 'violence'," Brody continued conversationally, "is a large part of everyday life in Canada. It's *big* business.

"But what would happen if the ordinary people got wise to the rules of the game? Wise to the invisible violence practiced on them by business, and those puppets of Big Business: governments.

"Are *you* — the business leaders of this country — telling the

166

poverty ridden majority of Canadians that 'violence' is their only choice?"

Brody was shouting at them again. "Violence to what end? To maintain *your* violence of the status quo ... or *theirs* to overthrow it?"

In the shocked silence a man speaking to a table companion could be heard. "He's a goddamn communist!"

Brody started again. "You men of the American Empire Club feel safe. Why not? In all the years ... the victims of your free enterprise violence have never fought back. They're impotent.

"You should remember," Brody concluded, "it is not power but its opposite — impotence — that leads to violence."

And he sat down.

There was no applause for Brody. Instead, Pete stood up and said in a loud voice: "Bloody fine speech, that!"

The president of the American Empire Club thanked Brody for his 'stimulating address' and reminded the membership that next week's speaker would be Professor Kismet Baruch, of the Harvard School of Business Management Techniques.

"I talked to Kismet," said the president, "the title of his speech will be: 'The Name of the Game is Producing for the Continental Market'. Kismet says it's a sector by sector approach to a common market as with the auto and energy pacts."

As the dining hall was being vacated, and people at the head table were milling about, Pete pushed his way to the front. "Great speech, Neil!" he said, and shook Brody's hand. And as quickly, he was tapping the president on the arm.

"Yes?" The president did not appear cordial.

"Excuse me," Pete told him. "I'm Mister Brody's manager. The secretary says you have to sign the cheque."

The president looked from Pete to Brody and then back to Pete. "Your cheque will be sent by mail; our customary procedure."

Pete's smile was friendly. "I asked your secretary to prepare it ... " he said as a small officious man hurried up holding the cheque. Pete took it, looked at it, then handed it to the president who pushed some dishes aside to give himself room to sign it.

"Thank you, sir," said Pete, taking the cheque and folding it. He turned at once to Brody. "You ready to go?"

Jan and Karen were waiting for them at the door. They kissed him and congratulated him. "Bloody fine speech, that!" Karen teased.

The plans called for Pete and Karen to go to Karen's meeting with the executive of Pension Power; Brody and Jan to return to the motel where Jan would work on her speech for that evening. As they were waiting for the elevator Pete thought of something. "Here," he said to Brody, handing him the cheque. "Cash it . . . now; before they decide to stop payment."

Brody got his first look at the cheque. It was for $2,000. He sighed.

"What's wrong?" Jan asked him.

He showed her the cheque. "They could have rented me, Lin Lee, *and* The Queen . . . for this much."

The results of Karen's afternoon meeting were exhilarating. Not only had the Pension Power executive been interested in what Karen had to say, they agreed to join forces with the People's Movement.

"They asked Pete to draft a press release announcing it," Karen told them. "Isn't it exciting?"

Brody had to admit that it was. But he had a question for Pete. "Will any press release issued by us ever see print?"

"I'm drafting it . . . Pension Power will release it. By the way," he added, "I phoned a friend at the U of T . . . he invited me to share a class with him."

"When?" Brody felt students were a waste of Pete's time.

"Tomorrow morning."

Pete's pleasure was so obvious that Brody decided he longed for the ego stimulation of university lecturing.

When they left the motel room for supper, they found a surveillance team sitting in an unmarked car nearby. The Mounties followed them to the restaurant. Later, they followed Jan and Brody downtown to the building where the Professional Women's Institute held their meetings.

Riding up in the elevator Brody remarked: "The Mounties will want to tape your speech."

"Sadie won't have any of *that*. Wait 'til you meet her."

Sadie Callaghan, chairwoman for the evening, was a 60-year-old lawyer who had pioneered Legal Aid for Welfare Mothers. She met them as they came off the elevator and Brody perceived at once what Jan had meant.

"Hey!" Sadie clasped Jan in a motherly bear hug. Then she turned to extend a hand of greeting to Brody. "So you're *it* . . . "

Sadie Callaghan was gregarious and forceful; she looked like a lady wrestler. Her bright coloured caftan billowed to the floor around her. "Neil, you can sit in there . . . go find yourself a chair." She pointed him in the direction of the meeting room and turned to Jan. The two friends began talking at once.

The professional girls were seated and ready for the meeting to start at the scheduled time. About 100 women attended; Brody guessed their average age at 35. All of them were well dressed and appeared confident of their own abilities; it was something they shared with the guest speaker.

Jan's speech was forthright and direct.

"I apologize for going over old ground," she told her audience, "the unresolved plight of the working woman . . . but it's important."

She described how women had been allowed into the economy in the first place: as low paid help in the teaching, nursing and clerical fields. Later — in times of war — they were hired in greater numbers and at better pay. But the gains were only temporary.

"Years ago," Jan continued, "we had our great emancipation . . . Women's Liberation.

"It went the same route as every other social reform movement. Women's Lib was bought off with tokenism and PR. We were co-opted.

"If you disagree with me . . . if you think women *are* better off than they were before Women's Lib . . . ask yourself some questions:

"Do women still earn less than men? Yes.

"Are women still used as cheap labour? Yes.

"Are working mothers any better off? No.

169

"Have our political leaders made any effort to redress our situation? No."

Jan told them, in cool dispassionate tones, that the economy was divided into two separate and unequal labour forces: male and female. And that although women, as a group, had better educational qualifications than men, men still earned twice as much.

"Half of the country's women are working," Jan said, "it means women are second-class labour."

She told her audience that salary discrimination extended to all professions, and cited medical care as an example. Whereas the low-pay professions of nursing and therapy were dominated by women, " . . . ninety-one per cent of doctors, and ninety-seven per cent of dentists . . . are men."

She said that in university teaching, men's salaries exceeded those of women by almost 50 per cent. In the business world, women made up less than ten per cent of managerial staff.

Jan reminded them of the plight of working mothers who were, she said, " . . . sentenced to long hours at low pay and to spend those hours worrying about day care for their children."

Jan itemized her proposals for change.

"More day care centres; child care costs deductible from income tax; maternity leave; and play areas in apartment buildings instead of pools and saunas."

Jan mentioned the special case of the mother on welfare. "Other forms of welfare — old age pension; baby bonus — are considered respectable," Jan said in measured tones of outrage, "yet women raising children on welfare are subjected to social abuse that amounts to punishment."

Toward the end she said there were many intelligent human beings — women — who should be replacing male parliamentarians who had gone "well beyond their levels of incompetence."

The audience laughed.

Jan told them about the People's Movement, and asked them to consider forming think groups to help save Canada from disintegration.

"What I'm advocating," Jan concluded, "is that we women take

170

over the shambles that men have produced in the governing of this country.

"And my first suggestion . . . I assume I'm permitted a suggestion . . . is a one-day work stoppage by women, to publicize the fact of our presence in the work force."

To Brody's amazement, the Professional Women's Institute voted to attempt that very thing: to organize the working women of Canada as a component part of the People's Movement, and to call a one-day strike of protest.

At their motel both Karen and Pete had things to show them.

"Pete was drafting the Pension Power release," Karen said, "so I went out and bought a paper."

"Did they cover Neil's speech?" Jan asked.

"No." Karen looked sympathetic as she offered Jan a page torn from the women's section of the paper. "It's about you."

by Judy Height

OTTAWA — Glamorous Sally Thorncrest, wife of mandarin high-riser Michael Thorncrest, and last-year winner of the Governor-General's Award for her Canada Council-financed novel *Lie Down and Love Me*, apparently did just that — but with a junior attache from a foreign embassy.

The cocktail circuit in the nation's capital is buzzing with the news of the appointment of René Hill as chairwoman of the Committee for New Stables for Canada's Equestrian Team.

Ms. Hill, wife of Finance Minister Roger Hill, said the federal government has agreed to provide $15 million for the Rockcliffe complex of stables and has donated the 98 acres of prime recreation land needed for practice riding.

"The Committee's task," said René, "is to raise funds for the jumps and things."

Jan Stewart, former Minister of Research and Development, spokeswoman for women's rights in Parliament,

made the classic woman's mistake: she
fell in love.

When her affair with an aging eccentric became too great an embar·
rassment to the Party, she threw up
her career to marry the man. How
'liberated' is that, Jan?

Jan didn't comment on it but turned to Pete. "Can we read your
press release?"

"It's good," Karen assured her. "It's really good."

Jan smiled at the younger woman. "Everything about your man
is good . . . isn't that true?"

When Jan finished reading it she handed the release to Brody.
"It *is* good," she told Pete.

TORONTO — Pension Power, the activist group for retireds and
others on fixed incomes, has joined forces with the People's Movement,
a new self-help organization based in Ottawa.

In announcing the merger of interests, Pension Power's outspoken
president, Sydney Langford, called on governments to better the lot of
old people in Canada by legislating the following:

— the right to work;

— a guaranteed income coupled with a guaranteed job;

— tax-free status at age 65;

— government funding for communal, tax-free living accommodation
for senior citizens;

— paid volunteers to help older people.

The 'volunteers' would be retired people who are willing to visit,
assist, or entertain people who, for reasons of health or infirmity,
cannot get around.

Over coffee they discussed their progress. They decided that
although Pete and Brody had alienated the Carleton faculty and the
American Empire Club, Karen and Jan had scored notable successes
with Pension Power and the Professional Women's Institute.

The restaurant was nearly empty. Through the front window they
could see the police car and the two faces behind the windshield.
"Canada . . ." Karen observed wryly, " . . . standing on guard for
we."

172

It gave them a laugh; still, the hovering presence of the police was discouraging. Jan returned to business. "How much can we accomplish tomorrow?" she asked.

"At noon hour you're speaking to the Women Against Men group," Pete told her. "I'll drop this news release at Pension Power on my way to U of T."

Brody asked Jan and Karen what they'd like to do while Pete was at the university.

"Let's talk to every unemployed person we can," suggested Karen.

Brody and Jan agreed to the proposal; and to her second proposal: that they do the same on the return trip to Ottawa. "I'll bet we could recruit ten new groups," Karen added.

Pete asked Jan what she proposed to tell the Women Against Men. "Do you think they'll listen?" Pete finished with a sly smile. "Now that you've done the unforgiveable . . . married?"

"They'll feel sorry for me," Jan said. "They'll feel I succumbed to conventional morality."

"What are you going to say to them?" Brody asked her.

"I guess I'll tell them what I think . . . not that it will recruit many of them to the People's Movement."

"What's that, Jan?" prompted Karen.

"They feel that women alone must do the job of liberating women; that all men are oppressors."

"I don't believe that," Karen said.

"Nor do I," Jan said. "So I expect to hear myself telling them that ideas are not segregated by sex; and that what we *need* are ideas."

"Is that where you'll ask their support? Ideas?"

"Mmm." Jan picked up her cup. "I don't think so. I may suggest that since ideas are mixed ideas, they should consider joining forces with a mixed group such as our own."

The talk turned to what Pete hoped to accomplish talking to university students. Brody didn't think Pete should waste his time.

"Why not?" Pete asked, his alert eyes fastened on Brody.

"Students are alienated," Brody replied, thinking of his visit to Carleton to talk with Professor Burwell.

"Well so are you," Karen said defensively.

"They take out their frustrations in petty and destructive ways," Brody said. "I don't think I'd want any of them around me."

"But surely our movement needs the drive and vitality of youth," Karen said.

Brody couldn't see it. "The only youth with drive and vitality I know is *you*," he told her.

"Not so, Neil," said Pete firmly.

"They're just lying around; waiting for their next government handout," Brody insisted.

"Oh, Neil!" said Karen in a hurt voice. She sat back, withdrawing from the argument.

"I'll bet I could find more people of your age 'lying around waiting for their next government handout' . . . than you could find young people," Pete argued.

Encouraged to do so by Jan prodding him in the ribs, Brody conceded. "I guess good people are where you find them," he admitted, "and age doesn't have a hell of a lot to do with it."

It was the most he could manage; he was convinced the young people of Canada would not help.

On the way back to Ottawa they stopped at Oshawa, Kingston and Brockville. In each of these cities they began with the crowds in the welfare offices, then spread their search for idling groups of unemployeds. Like evangelists, Pete, Karen, Jan and Brody talked to these unutilized people . . . the 'rejects' as they called themselves in factory parlance . . . and invited them to help save Canada.

The four made an impact. All they were asking was the time and ideas of unemployed people. A surprising number of these were prepared to start discussion/idea groups of their own; and to communicate the results to the People's Movement headquarters in Ottawa. The decisions came despite the threatening presence of the Mounties hovering close enough to hear.

"Remember," Brody kept repeating, "the solutions to the problems lie with the people."

Bad news awaited them in Ottawa: their headquarters had been wrecked. Ron, his face battered and covered with scabs, told them about it. "I had a hunch something might happen . . . so I decided to sleep here overnight. Sure enough . . . the Mounties came to call."

Brody felt more anger about Ron's beating than he had about his own. "Did they take anything?" he asked.

"They were looking for files; when they didn't find any, they acted like a bunch of hoodlums . . . broke up the place."

"Where did you get *this* furniture?" Brody asked.

The expensive furniture Jan had bought had been replaced with well used but nonetheless serviceable items.

"The people!" Ron's good humour seemed misplaced amid his bruises.

"I wonder what *my* place looks like," Jan wondered aloud.

Ron told them that in their absence he had recruited three more groups of unemployeds. "I don't know who all these people are. I don't figure I need to know." He turned to Pete. "You know the newspaper you wanted?"

"Yes?"

"You've got it."

"Where?"

"A guy with a printing press . . . bankrupt years ago . . . couldn't sell his equipment."

"We've got money for paper and printing supplies," Brody offered, thinking of his $2,000.

"Don't need it. The guy has enough for two or three editions," Ron said. He turned to Pete again. "You were going to collate ideas, remember? You don't have to."

"No?" Pete was surprised.

"Listen!" Ron leaned forward on his chair. "All over this country . . . the last twenty years . . . small newspapers have folded; taken over by the big circulation dailies."

"Printing presses available?" Brody asked.

"More than presses, Neil! Editors . . . writers . . . printing tradesmen. All of them out of work; none of them needed."

"They'll never get publication permits," Brody pointed out.

"That's right, Neil. Every one of them will be published underground and bootlegged. As the cops close up one shop, another will open somewhere else."

175

"How do we get hold of these people?" Pete asked.

Ron spoke to all of them. "You don't, for God's sake. You don't!" And when no one answered he added: "It's out of your hands!"

Ron told them his theory that, once started, the movement to get out of work Canadians thinking, talking, and doing for themselves would be out of the control of anyone.

"It's 'People Power'. Once we get this thing going . . . and it's going now . . . watch it go."

When Brody and Jan arrived home that night it was to find the apartment all but dismantled.

"I wonder what they were looking for in the mattress?" Jan asked, poking her finger in a knife slash.

They had just begun to clean things up when Pete called him on the phone. "A Mrs. Redke, in Toronto . . . she wants you to call her."

"I don't know any Mrs. Redke."

"She says you're a friend of her son Rudy."

Rudy. He tried to recall. A basement came to mind . . . running water . . . comrades Rudy and Lionel.

"I remember him, Pete . . . give me the number."

Mrs. Redke told him that Rudy and his friend Lionel had been arrested the night before. She wondered whether Brody could use his 'influence' in Ottawa to have the boys put in juvenile detention, rather than sent to the camps for adult offenders up North.

"They're only sixteen," the worried mother said, "but our lawyer says the Civil Unrest Act doesn't recognize age. Could you *do* something, Mister Brody?"

He promised to do what he could; when Jan asked him afterward what this might be, he admitted he didn't know.

As they were going to bed the phone rang again. This time it was Lin Lee, in Hay River, telling him *The Queen* had been sold and asking him where he should send Brody's $20,000.

176

Chapter 10

The days that followed were hectic. The founders of the People's Movement, and Ron Taylor, worked early to late. The government had cut Ron from the welfare rolls so the People's Movement hired him as its one employee. The only thing he missed, he told them, was the handouts at the Chinese Embassy. And he wryly commented: "My kids miss the propaganda comic books they put in the parcels."

Brody tried to help Rudy and Lionel. He called Sgt. Godfrey, who told him the case was being 'processed' . . . and agreed with him that 16 *was* young, but that their activities were 'dangerous to the democratic state'.

Brody called the only mandarin he knew: Reid-Wilkinson of the Privy Council Office. Reid-Wilkinson, when he finally returned Brody's calls, was unsympathetic. He knew of the arrest of the young Maoists, but was unwilling to intervene with 'Justice'. The one thing he did say, and which Brody was able to pass on to Rudy's mother, was that the boys were still in the Toronto area.

The $20,000 Brody got for his half of *The Queen* went for a second advertisement in the major dailies across Canada. The ad invited the public to a founding convention of the People's Party . . . as well as to an Armistice Day rally on Parliament Hill the night before.

The advertisement:

Put Canada First!

The Canadian public is invited to a mass meeting of the People's Movement in Ottawa, November 12-13, for the purpose of founding a People's Party.

Based on the principle that 'The solutions to Canada's problems lie with the people', the movement has mushroomed into its component structure of 10-person discussion/idea groups across Canada.

If you wish to start a People's Movement group, do so, it costs nothing. If you wish to forward the results of the deliberations of your group to our Ottawa headquarters, we will send them to People's Movement newspapers for publication.

Among ideas received to date:

Agriculture: All produce to be marketed and sold by the government; farmers to be paid as civil servants.

Native peoples: Indians and Inuit to be given full responsibility for the environmental custody of wilderness and recreation areas of Canada.

Housing: Land bank and life lease arrangement; housing standards and styles determined by local councils.

Regionalism: Hierarchy of governments reversed; federal government to be a service organization for provincial and municipal governments; the municipalities to carry the larger fiscal responsibility.

Education: Salaried university education for those who can meet the standards; job-training by professions (e.g. medicine; engineering; business).

Industry: To be run by worker councils.

Small business: Interest free government loans for capitalization of small business ventures.

Defence: Disband the Department of National Defence; use the $10 billion annual budget to repatriate Canadian industry from U.S. interests.

Come to Ottawa for the Armistice Day rally on Parliament Hill the evening of November 11; attend the founding convention of the People's Party November 12-13. For details write to: People's Movement Headquarters, Box 4600, Ottawa KIA OH2; phone (613) 233-3831.

The funding of their headquarters came from the speaking fees Pete charged for Brody and Jan. If they weren't engaged on one of these, they joined Karen talking to unemployeds. Their evenings were usually spent forwarding the news and ideas coming in from groups to others across the country.

Although the standard speaker's fee on the university circuit was only $500, Pete booked Brody for a couple of them per week. It must have been, Brody deduced, because Pete's heart was still in teaching.

Student audiences liked Brody, in about the same inverse ratio as he disliked them. They, apparently, liked to be told that the hope of Canada did not lie with youth, but with the old people.

They applauded when he told them students in Canada were bought and paid for with government grants, and cheered when he said the institutions of higher learning were just holding pens . . . keeping the youth off welfare rolls and off the job market.

"Meanwhile," Brody concluded that particular point, "the universities provide employment for educated adults."

No disciplined thinkers could result from the continued watering down of content, Brody said, and added that students pampered themselves with 'self-centred individualism'.

"The Cult of Individualism assures that no responsibility is ever apportioned . . . " Brody insisted, " . . . and makes absolutely certain that no leaders will ever evolve."

Brody never got to finish a speech to a university audience. Sometimes he barely got started when the student fascist elements — led by Mountie provocateurs — would begin shouting and picking fights in the audience; throwing chairs, or turning on the sprinkler systems. Once, at Queen's, they used tear gas.

At York University one rainy night in late October, Brody was talking about his idea of Canada providing a World University. The idea was to educate people of the third world; the people having been chosen by their own governments for the free education provided by Canada. He tried to talk about it in the intermittent quiet spells when students weren't shouting at each other across the auditorium.

Brody hesitated, then started to talk about the Police State. "In

Ottawa," he said, "our telephones are bugged. Outside our headquarters is a police car. It monitors every conversation inside, and they photograph everyone who enters or leaves.

"My home has been broken into and vandalized; so was our headquarters. When they found someone there . . . they beat him up."

He was interrupted by heckling shouts of: "Cry, baby!" and: "Where's your People Power?"

Brody pointed in the direction of the taunts. "A police state encroaches slowly," he said, measuring the words, "and first it erodes, and then it finally desregards the rule of law."

He was talking, of course, about the Mounties, but the fascists in the hall thought he was talking about them. They burst into raucous shouts, banging chairs against the walls, and finally ended up charging down the aisle toward the stage brandishing their chairs at Brody.

Surprised at the way things were going, Brody strode to the stairs where he met the first chair-wielder on his way up. Brody plucked the chair from the boy's grasp and hit him with a fist that didn't travel ten inches.

As the victim hit the aisle at the foot of the stairs Brody, swinging it, let the folding chair fly at the second wave of rioters. The cartwheeling mass of metal hit two boys. The noise it made bouncing off them, plus their yelps of pain and shock, stunned both attackers and audience.

He saw Jan hurrying toward him along the front row of seats, but he remained on the steps glaring at the frightened student rioters.

"You've killed him!" quavered one of them.

Brody knew the boy wasn't dead. "Leave him there," he commanded.

He held out his hand to Jan who joined him on the stage. She was pale, but calm.

"Come on," Brody said to her. "I'll finish my speech."

The student audience was standing, looking at the corner where the one-punch fight had occurred.

With Jan at his side Brody told them: "Freedom for all Canadians — all the time — cannot exist unless everyone is subject to the rule of law.

"No person, no class, no group or sect . . . " Brody pointed at the chair-wielders now huddling round their unconscious companion, " . . . nobody can be above the law."

The boy had a broken jaw. His parents launched a lawsuit against Brody and the university. Pete took him off the campus circuit.

Not only were Brody and Jan lovers, they were a mutual admiration society. Her presence in the audience thrilled him. She prompted his most creative thoughts, the spontaneity of which surprised himself.

And he was just as happy to be sitting as part of her audience. These were usually women's groups and they listened intently as Jan told it as it truly was.

"A woman has to make a deal in this society," Jan said, "that deal is marriage." And she said that society has cruel punishments for the woman who doesn't catch a man.

Usually Jan stressed the exploitation theme. "There are no breaks . . . management will keep a secretary — who is really an executive assistant — at a secretary's salary."

Nor did Jan forget the women who stay at home to raise the nation's children. She told them that if the People's Party came to power " . . . the government will pay housewives a comparable salary."

Brody got the chance to address 300 Prairie farmers who came to Ottawa for another useless protest. In the auditorium Pete rented for the occasion Brody told the Farmers' Union about their problems. Since many of these same problems had been common to Lin Lee and himself, Brody's rage was real.

He started by pointing out the soaring cost of farm land; the staggering prices of farm machinery; the mortgages "no one will live to see paid off.

"The farmer has no standard working day, no overtime, no vacations, no paid holidays," Brody said. "He has no security and he carries the burden of taxes for his community.

"Insurance costs are out of reach; and the government expects you to do its bookkeeping."

Brody was the only man in Ottawa who seemed to give a damn and the Farmers' Union delegates hung on his every word.

"If we get our People's Party elected as the government of this country we'll change the system which makes peasants out of farmers," he told them.

"We'll legislate against corporate farming . . . the vertically integrated food companies will be banned.

"Instead, we'll rationalize the food retail industry by having the government own it.

"We'll use land banking with lifetime lease back; your children get first crack at the lease when you die.

"All agricultural produce will be marketed and sold by the government; farmers will be paid straight salaries the same as any other government employee.

"If the farmers of a community wish to do so, they can divide their labour in any kind of collective farming arrangement they, and their families, wish to make."

Brody had to stop while his audience cheered, whistled and applauded. It was not often that Brody — who tended to batter his audiences with unpleasant facts about themselves — evoked applause. It surprised him.

"Do you agree with me?" he asked the farmers.

Another storm of applause swept the auditorium.

"Okay," Brody told them, "I'm going to tell you that every one of those ideas was sent in to our People's Movement headquarters from a group in rural Eastern Ontario . . . we don't even know their names."

And when the applause died down, Brody said: "It's proof that the farmers of this country, given the chance to do so, could solve the problems of agriculture."

Since neither the Minister of Agriculture, the Prime Minister, or anyone else connected with the government found time to talk to the delegation, Brody's speech was the high point of their trip to Ottawa. When they went back to the Prairies, they were People's Movement converts.

One busy morning Pete hung up the phone and turned to Brody. "How do you like scientists?"

"They're okay, I guess."

"*I'm* a scientist, you know."

"You hurt his feelings, Neil," joked Karen from the corner table where she was stuffing envelopes.

"I'm sorry," Brody apologized to his friend the biologist. "What about scientists?"

"The Society of Concerned Scientists are in town for their annual hair-rending and teeth-gnashing; they need someone to scourge them," Pete said.

"Shouldn't Jan talk to them?"

"They want to be scourged," Pete told him. "Jan is too loveable."

Jan came over and patted Pete's beard. "You're right, I feel too loveable to be mean to poor scientists. Come on Neil, I'll help you with a speech."

"Wait a minute. Why do you think the scientists want to be punished?"

"Only once a year," Pete said sardonically, "the rest of the time they're happy to have sold their professional souls."

Brody was being asked to fill in for another scientific soul-saver who had erred by trusting Canada's airline to get him to Ottawa on time. It was an after lunch speech and Brody knew that he was merely being asked to entertain, not shock.

So he told them of the twin science-related failures of the past decade which, unattended, now threatened the world: pollution and ecology.

"Pollution has become a problem of such horrendous implications that only a global limitation on production can ensure Man's very survival," he said.

And about the ecological crisis: "Man's faith in technology is misplaced," Brody said. "World conferences attempting to deal with the problems — food resources, for one — are always unsuccessful.

"The last whale has been exterminated; the last cod; the last tuna . . . all victims of unrestrained technology."

Brody questioned the efficacy of government.

"It's problematical whether any democratic form of government

183

— dependent on patronage and compromise, saddled with outdated priorities — is capable of more than what our own government has done . . . that is, nothing.

"Governments tend to ignore the advice of scientists. You can expect this any time the facts do not coincide with what the politicians want to believe."

The scientists applauded him.

So Brody told them why the public doesn't trust scientists. "People are suspicious," he said. "They see Science as another threat . . . along with Big Government and Big Business."

Low grey clouds, pushed by a cold wind, crowded the Peace Tower as Brody, Ron Taylor and a gang of unemployeds worked to finish the speakers platform on Parliament Hill. It was from here that Brody and Jan would address the pre-convention rally of delegates that evening.

Over at the War Memorial an honour guard, a shivering padre, and a listless brass band went through the Armistice Day rite. It was sad. As a splatter of rain hit the planking someone asked: "Do they bring the Army in from Petawawa for Armistice Day?"

A fleet of U.S.-built, Canadian Armed Forces trucks rolled by on the street. Each of them was filled with combat-armed troops. Brody had a feeling of unease. "They aren't here for a ceremony," he said to his friends. "Must be an exercise."

When the gang had finished they walked back to headquarters where Karen and Jan had a 'Welcome People's Party Delegates' banner spread out front, and coffee and doughnuts inside. As the work crew trooped in Pete was on the phone arguing with someone. The room was hushed as he concluded with: "If we have to cancel, we will . . . but not just yet." He hung up.

"What happened, Pete?" Brody asked.

"The government just revoked our permit to assemble."

"Tonight on the Hill?"

Pete nodded. "They gave us that permit three weeks ago."

"What's their reason?"

" 'Dangerous elements in the People's Movement'," Pete said bitterly. "We threaten the 'peace and good order' of the Hill area."

184

The room was crowded with out of town delegates. There were too many people for a strategy discussion so Jan asked everyone to go sight-see Ottawa.

"Do you want us to take down the platform?" Ron asked Brody as his crew filed out the door again.

"Leave it for now; and thanks," Brody said.

He turned to Pete. "Cancel the rally and concentrate on the convention tomorrow."

"Hell, no!" Pete disagreed; he'd worked hard these weeks. "We've already been invited to share the rally in the market."

"What rally?" Brody wanted to know.

"The student group at Ottawa University is holding a Keep Quebec in Canada rally."

"What group is that?" Brody was suspicious; Ottawa University had never been heard of in relation to the People's Movement.

The room was silent. Jan poured a coffee and handed it to Brody.

"You just don't like university students," Pete said. "You don't trust them."

"Damn right I don't."

"They're not *all* fascist bastards," Pete said. "This group is trying to help us out."

"Who are they?"

"I don't know their names; but hell, Neil . . . we don't know the names of most of our *own* people."

"When did they invite us to join their rally?" Brody demanded.

"This morning."

"We had our *own* rally going then."

"They were just extending a friendly invitation . . . you do want to keep Quebec in Confederation, don't you?"

"Too late for that," Brody snapped. "I don't like it. Something's not right."

"Come on, Neil. It's just your bias against students."

"I don't mind students," Brody said, "it's the goddamn Mounties they have in their groups."

"*All* the groups have Mounties."

Brody sighed. "Okay . . . have it your way. But I don't want anything to do with it."

"They want you to address the rally."

"No."

"Why not?" Pete was surprised. It was the first time Brody had ever refused to speak.

"Tomorrow . . . at our own meeting . . . when we talk about founding a People's Party; then Jan and I will talk."

Brody was adamant, so Pete didn't push him. "Will you come tonight?"

Brody looked at Jan, who nodded. "Okay," he said. "We'll go to watch; but that's it."

The spatter of rain had become showers by the time Brody and Jan set out for the rally that evening. They were tired from the pace leading up to the People's Party convention, and Brody was discouraged by what he felt was a change in Pete's attitude. They discussed it as they walked.

"Pete isn't really trying to be the party leader," Jan said. "But he worries that you don't want the job badly enough."

"He's right . . . I don't want it. But if I'm the best person for the job . . . I'll do it."

"Good." She squeezed his arm.

"I think you should be leader of the People's Party," he told her reprovingly. They'd been over this ground many times.

"Canada isn't ready for a woman leader," Jan said in a matter of fact voice.

The cold wind was funnelling between the ancient stone buildings that surrounded the market area. Brody was glad Jan had bought them new jackets that were lightweight but warm.

"Look, Neil! There's hardly any people."

The crowd of Ottawa U students hoped for hadn't materialized. Instead, about 500 people, almost all of them delegates to the People's Party convention, were wandering the area in front of a pipe and planking scaffold on which stood Pete and Karen with a group of students. Virtually the whole market was lit by giant flood lights, a fact which re-aroused Brody's suspicions.

"Where would students get all this stuff?"

He was becoming more distrustful by the second. "Look," he

186

nudged her, nodding in the direction of a plain-clothes cop holding a communicator radio.

There were several TV crews set up on scaffolding. Brody took Jan over to one of these camera set-ups; there was no identification on any of the equipment, nor on the crew.

On the hunch that the film crew weren't what they appeared to be, Brody spoke to the man in charge. "Corporal?"

"Sir?" the young man said, coming over to them.

"I've forgotten your name."

"Sergeant Weatherby, Signals Corps."

"I guess we haven't met," Brody said. "Is everything ready?"

"Yes, sir." The sergeant smiled, and added: "As long as the power units stay up."

When the Sergeant had gone Jan asked: "What are 'power units'?"

"Electrical generators." Brody started toward the speakers' platform. "I've got to stop Pete."

"Wait, Neil." She held him back.

"What's wrong?"

"What do you want Pete to do?"

"Get the hell out of here." Brody looked round them; the more he looked, the more Mounties in plain-clothes he saw. "Come on," he said to her.

"Pete knows what he wants," Jan told him. "And we knew the Mounties would be present at any kind of a rally."

Brody hesitated. What she said was correct; when they'd planned their own rally they'd predicted as many Mounties as People's Party delegates.

"I should talk to him anyway," Brody worried.

"Don't." She tugged him in the opposite direction. "Pete's happy up there with his students."

Brody glowered in the direction of the speakers stand where Pete and Karen were helping with the microphones.

"Those droopy moustaches don't fool me," he told Jan. "They're Mounties."

"If you tell Pete his friends are spies, he'll accuse you of hating students."

187

"I don't *hate* them . . . I just don't *trust* them."

"Same thing." Jan started towing him away. "Pete feels that any movement to reform in Canada has to be based on the youth."

"We'll wait a long goddamn time . . . " Brody started.

"Shush!" she said.

They watched the proceedings from the shelter of a doorway across the market. The proceedings didn't take long. The first speaker, a lanky student with hanging hair and moustache, made an emotional pitch — in French — calling on Quebec to remain in Confederation. No one applauded.

Brody stifled the impulse to comment on the chances of Quebec wanting to re-negotiate Confederation.

Next Pete welcomed the delegates to the People's Party founding convention, reminding them of the time and place of the sessions the next day, and ending by thanking them for coming to Ottawa. This time the crowd responded with applause.

"Good for him," Brody remarked. "He kept it short."

"It's too cold for long speeches," Jan said.

Standing that far from the speakers' platform, they were spectators, not participants. They saw a man step out of the crowd, climb the scaffolding to the platform, and walk confidently to the mikes.

"Who's this guy?" Brody wondered aloud.

The man told the crowd he was a People's Party delegate, a tax paying citizen, and had come to Ottawa a day early to "attend a rally on Parliament Hill!

"That's *our* Hill," the man shouted. "We pay for it, we *own* it!"

And after several more minutes of this kind of emotional diatribe — to which even Brody responded with a gut feeling of outrage at the government's sudden banning of their rally — the man ended by shouting: "Let's go to the Hill!"

The crowd cheered.

"Hold it!" Brody yelled, starting out of the doorway.

"Neil!" Jan clung to his arm. "It's too late . . . everyone's going."

The crowd of People's Party delegates — for there were few students — led by Pete, Karen, Ron and his crew of unemployeds, was heading for Parliament Hill.

188

"We're not going," he told her as they stood watching the exodus.

"Look," he said, pointing. On a far rooftop was a man with a walkie-talkie radio, walking and talking.

Jan shivered, holding with both arms to his. "Something's going to happen, Neil."

An army jeep lurched out of a loading rampway several stores down and roared past them, lights out, toward Ottawa's main street which led to Parliament Hill.

"The goddamn army!" Brody said.

"What about it?"

He told her about the convoy of troop vehicles they'd seen arriving that morning.

"Come on," he said, leading her by the hand.

They walked the dark street which paralleled, by a block, the street being followed by the excited crowd. Brody chose another darkened doorway to view Rideau Street leading past the Chateau Laurier to the Hill. The crowd was already streaming past the Chateau, blocking traffic as it overflowed the sidewalk onto the street.

"Look there," Brody said, "and there."

An army truck was parked on the sidewalk at one intersection; another protruded from a dark laneway farther along the street.

Just as the last of the crowd disappeared into the entrance gate of the East Block, a whitish glow lit the skyline and a staccato burst of gunfire echoed down the street toward them.

They heard screams coming from the Hill; saw scurrying crowds silhouetted against the glow jamming into the street again. Running to meet them were soldiers, with rifles; Brody and Jan could see them emerging from the store-fronts and alleyways. More shots — intermittent, now — crackled. The soldiers were capturing fleeing people. Brody and Jan saw rifles being used as clubs.

"Neil! Oh God . . . can this be happening?"

Brody didn't answer. Instead, he turned her toward him. "Will you go home?"

"No." Her face was pale. "Not unless you go with me."

"They're killing people up there."

"*Our* people," she said. "Come on. There must be *some* way we can stop it."

Because they were walking purposefully toward the Hill the soldiers paid no attention to them. They saw bodies being slung into the backs of army trucks while others, more lucky, were able to climb in. Many of the prisoners were bleeding and one old man was cursing. "Murderers! Goddamn murderers!" he screamed.

"Shut up," grunted a hard-paunch soldier clouting the old man into the truck.

The army squad guarding the East Block gate let Brody and Jan in without comment. The entire Hill area was lit by floodlights mounted on the escarpment and on the roofs of the East and West Blocks. On the main lawn huddled People's Party delegates. The rifle-equipped soldiers encircling the prisoners allowed Jan and Brody to join their friends.

"Here's Neil," said a voice with relief.

"Where's Pete Ranallo?" Brody asked anyone.

"Pete's dead." It was Ron who answered him. "Come here."

Pete was dead, Karen was dying. Five others had been killed and at least ten more people were lying bleeding on the cold black grass. Brody knelt beside Pete's body; Jan was on her knees beside Karen who was breathing wheezily through bloody froth.

"Don't lift the coat," Ron told him. "The bastards are using dum-dums; they got Pete through the eye."

Brody stood up and looked round. The soldiers had them herded. A cannister was steaming away over by the West Block.

"What's that for?" he asked Ron.

"Riot gas; but it's too windy."

"What are they planning to do?"

"I don't know, Neil. They're having a conference about us." Ron pointed at the speakers platform they'd built that morning. Police and army officers were standing on it.

"Something's got to be done for our wounded," Brody said. He started for the platform.

"Hold it, mister!" A young soldier shoved the muzzle of his rifle in Brody's stomach. "Get back in the circle."

Brody slowly pushed the rifle to one side. "Who's in charge?" he asked.

The soldier nodded toward the speakers platform. "Up there," he said.

As Brody approached the platform he called out: "Who's in charge here?"

A policeman wearing a white visored helmet came down the stairs. Beside him came another one carrying a riot gun.

"Stay where you are, Mister Brody."

It was Sgt. Godfrey.

"I want to talk to you, Sergeant," said Brody, walking close enough to converse.

A spotlight on the platform was suddenly turned on in Brody's face. He didn't see the gun-butt come out of the dazzling light to crumple his face.

Pain, darkness, a prickly blanket, the bunk, the toilet, were Brody's new existence. He lay in a half-real state of pain and fever; dreams melting into hallucination. When his fever was up he dreamt his old nightmare: fire in the cockpit. When he was cold he dreamt of being trapped in a downed aircraft in the sub-Arctic winter. Most of his dreams were of traps.

Brody's face had been crushed by the gun-butt. His teeth, the bone shelf above the teeth, his nose and both cheekbones, had all been shattered. And he was blind. He became aware of this as time passed and hunger came to clear the confusion from his mind. The hungrier he got, the more lucid he became.

He wondered, endlessly: where's Jan? Was she trying to reach him?

Thirsty, he rolled himself off the bunk and felt his way along the bars to the wall, and along the wall to the sink. The tap in the sink supplied cold water; he scooped a handful onto the shards and hanging nerves, the remains of his front teeth. The pain made him sick and again he was on his knees, head in the toilet bowl, retching weakly and helplessly.

This time he managed to crawl back to the bunk before passing out.

He awoke to the sound of a door opening; footsteps approaching his cell; a key in a lock. He sensed two people.

"You awake?" one of them asked.

"Yes," said Brody. It came out 'yeth'.

"Can you walk?"

"Yeth."

"Come on; we'll help you if you need it."

"Shooth," Brody said, sitting up.

"Under the bunk, Frank," said the same voice. "Bring his jacket, too."

The man named Frank helped him put on his shoes, then draped the jacket over his shoulders. After a few tottery steps he got the feeling of walking without groping, depending on the men to keep him from walking into things.

The short corridor led to the door he'd heard open before. When they went through it he realized they were in a cell block housing many people.

"Hey, Neil!" someone called.

"Jesus, Neil . . . what did they do to you?"

Brody didn't recognize the voices. But he tried a question anyway. "Wha' happen'?"

Several of the prisoners tried to answer at once. He heard two of them.

"Four hundred of us in the can, Neil!"

"Across Canada . . . they're rounding us up!"

"Shut up!" shouted the man at Brody's side.

They stopped for another locked door; as it opened, his friends called to him again.

"Luck, Neil."

"Hang tough."

"Bye, Neil."

Brody held up his big right hand, fist clenched. The door closed behind him on a spontaneous cheer. Poor bastards, thought Brody.

They took a short elevator ride; then down a hallway to a room which — by the sound the door made opening and closing — did not contain much furniture.

"You'll have to wait," the man said.

"Chair?" Brody asked, conserving words. The air hurt when he opened his mouth. They shoved a straightback chair into the backs of his knees. It felt good to sit down.

He imagined what the scene was going to be: interrogation. He recalled the wartime phrase pertaining to capture: 'Name rank and serial number'. Behind him the door closed as his guards left and he immediately fell into a doze.

A door opened elsewhere in the room, awakening him. Footsteps . . . more than two people . . . chairs being arranged. When everyone was settled, the interrogation began.

"Brody?"

The voice was familiar.

"It's Orlando Orbach."

"Who elth?"

"Sergeant Godfrey."

Brody didn't respond. He remembered Godfrey's face behind the visor of his riot helmet; the dazzle of spotlight; the gun-butt.

"Brody?" said Godfrey. "I'm sorry. The man thought you were attacking me."

Brody waved mental farewell to his teeth and two perfectly good eyes. "Who'th the other guy?" Brody lisped. "Your Thee.I.A. advither?"

No answer.

Orbach cleared his throat before starting. "Brody? The Prime Minister invoked the War Measures Act."

"When?"

"He invoked it retroactively . . . after your mob attacked the Hill."

That would account for the 400 people imprisoned in Ottawa. How many elsewhere in Canada?

"Brody?"

"Mm?"

"You're a sick man."

Brody nodded. He agreed with the diagnosis.

"I mean mentally sick . . . subversively sick."

Brody didn't answer. He couldn't think of anything to say worth the pain of opening his mouth.

"Dangerously sick."

Brody listened, wondering why Orbach was going on like this.

"This movement you were leading," Orbach continued. "It's dangerous."

"Watch the old folkth," Brody murmured.

"What?"

"Old folkth . . . dangerouth."

"Brody . . . "

"Working motherth."

"Brody," there was sadness in the General's voice. "I'm trying to explain something to you."

"What?"

"Canada and the United States together. What's wrong with that?"

And when Brody didn't reply: "Our Canadian way of life depends on our membership in the American industrial empire. Can't you see that?"

Brody was feeling woozy. And arguing was not going to change any decisions about his fate. The decisions — he felt sure — had been made.

"What is good for the United States *is* good for Canada," Orbach persisted.

Brody shook his head.

"Can't you talk, Brody?"

"Endth equalth meanth ethic," Brody succeeded with the last word. "The U.ETH. ethic . . . " He struggled through a mangled mouth to explain Canada-U.S. relationships. "Exth-ploitive arrangementh with thatellithe like Canada."

The effort exhausted him; his head buzzed and seemed to wobble.

"Brody, look." The irony was unintended. "North America is the last bastion of democracy. We're locked in an economic war with totalitarian socialism."

When Brody failed to comment, Orbach changed the subject. He seemed truly to want Brody to understand. "The government is going to bring in more welfare legislation."

If Brody could have smiled, he would have. He longed to tell Orbach that more social engineering would not change things. That capitalism is a dead and gone force. That Canadians have but one option: capitalism *or* socialism. And that there can be no in-between step because capitalism — the greed motive — always corrupts it.

"Brody?"

He lifted his drooping head.

"We're sending you to a hospital for the criminally insane. It's a three-hour drive; you'll go by car."

He heard chairs scrape as the three men stood up. Brody had a panicky thought. "My wife?"

"She's under arrest, too. I'm sorry." The door Brody had entered opened, and two men came in. As Brody stood up, Orbach said: "Goodbye." He hesitated, then added: "You're a very brave man ... courageous."

Brody sighed. Orbach didn't know that courage is a secondary virtue.

The two men walked on either side of him. As they stepped outside the building, one said to him: "Twelve steps to the pavement; the car is right there."

The cold November air felt good; it re-aroused his hunger pangs. He heard a car door open.

"Front seat, Mister Brody. We'll ride three up front."

Since the other two were as big as he, the front seat was crowded. Brody had no idea of where they were starting from; he assumed it was Mountie headquarters. If so, they'd probably hit the freeway in a minute or two.

"This okay?" the driver said, abruptly slowing the car.

"Okay, Frank. Stop here."

The tension in the man's voice communicated a warning to Brody. He felt the man on his right squirming round to face him; at the same instant he felt a blow accompanied by a flash of white-hot pain high on the shoulder. It was a needle.

As the flush of pain spread downward through his arm and across his upper body he was aware of the driver getting out, then reaching back into the car to drag him across the seat. The other man pushed.

"Grab onto the wheel, Mister Brody," the man said politely. And to the driver: "Pull his foot over."

Brody was scarcely aware of the arrangements as the drug-induced seizure paralyzed his chest. Pain flooded his body; he was choking with pain. Convulsively he gripped the wheel. He was screaming as his body snapped rigid and his left foot drove the gas pedal to the floor. He was dead before the car hit the concrete wall.

OTTAWA (CP) — Neil Brody, aged 60, apparently died of a heart seizure during an escape attempt from National Security Detention headquarters late Thursday night.

He was found slumped over the wheel of a government-owned car which had collided with a concrete abutment near a ramp leading up to Ottawa's expressway.

Mr. Brody was a much-decorated bomber pilot of World War II. Following the war he operated an air charter company in the Northwest Territories.

When his business collapsed earlier this year Mr. Brody came to Ottawa where he acquired local notoriety as an eccentric reformer.

He was being held in protective custody following an Armistice Day disturbance on Parliament Hill, pending psychiatric tests and treatment.

He leaves a wife, the former Jan Stewart. There are no children.